Along Friendly Roads

Along Friendly Roads

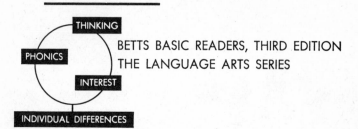

BETTS BASIC READERS, THIRD EDITION
THE LANGUAGE ARTS SERIES

EMMETT A. BETTS — Research Professor in Education and Lecturer in Psychology, School of Education, University of Miami, Coral Gables 46, Florida

CAROLYN M. WELCH — Reading Consultant, Henry S. West Laboratory School, University of Miami, Coral Gables 46, Florida

ILLUSTRATED BY: *Betty Alden, Elinore Blaisdell, Hertha Depper, Dorothy Grider, William D. Hayes, Helen John, Albert D. Jousset, Violet Jousset, Walter Howard Knapp, Jane March, Bob Meyers, Reta Brigham Morey, Christine Price, Mary Stevens, Erna Ward, Kurt Werth.*

Cover and frontispiece: *Oscar Liebman*

AMERICAN BOOK COMPANY

New York   Cincinnati   Atlanta   Dallas   Millbrae

5   7   9   11   13   15   S.P.   16   14   12   10   8   6

Take-off . . . . *Margaret Troy* 6

STORIES

By the Sea

The Treasure Hunt . . . . . *Berta and Elmer Hader* 14
Little Whitetail . . . . . . *Elsie Grant Henson* . 20
The King of Smithland . . . . *Walter R. Brooks* . . 26
How the Bridge Helped . . . *Mildred Lawrence* . . 33
The Long Road to Rivertown . *Elizabeth Coatsworth* . 40
Let's Make Gus Smile . . . . *Mildred Lawrence* . . 46
PHONICS 330
THINKING ACTIVITIES 346

Our Southland

A Train Ghost . . . . *Florence Hayes* . . . 54
The Tom Thumb Train . . . *Jack Bechdolt* . . . 61
Something to Do . . . . . . *Val Teal* 68
New Homes in Kentucky . . . *Edna McGuire* . . . 74
Winter in the South . . . . . *James S. Tippett* . . . 81
Step-Along . . . . *May Justus* 82
A Tall Tale from the High Hills *Ellis Credle* 89
Bright-Eyes, the Little Raccoon . *Allen Chaffee* 93
The Story Teller . . . . . . *Fable* 100
PHONICS 332
THINKING ACTIVITIES 347

River Days

Slow Poke . . . . *Charlie May Simon* . . 106
The Bee Man . . . . *Isabel Proudfit* . . . 114
Pepperminta the Great . . . . *Miriam M. Swain* . . 121
Three Cheers! It's Spring! . . . *Earl Marvin Rush* . . 129
Sleeping Beauty . . . . . . *Fairy Tale* 136
The River . . . . *Aileen Fisher* 144
Tom Edison . . . . *Covelle Newcomb* . . 146
Billy Whitemoon . . . . . . *Ruth M. Tabrah* . . . 153
PHONICS 335
THINKING ACTIVITIES 348

Rolling Plains

Dick Follows His Nose . . . . *LeGrand Henderson* . 162
Johnny Big-Pockets . . . . . *Neil Anderson* . . . 169
The Forgot Store . . . . . . *Val Teal* 176
A Letter from Grandfather . . *Glenn O. Blough* . . . 184
A Tree for Christmas . . . . *Marion Gartler* . . . 189
The Moving House . . . . . *Dorothy Aldis* . . . 197
Bill Cody, Winner of the West . *Frank L. Beals* . . . 198
The Mule-eared Squirrel . . . *George Cory Franklin* . 206
PHONICS 337
THINKING ACTIVITIES 350

Cowboy Trails

The Song That Cows Do Not Like   *LeGrand Henderson* . 214
A Carol for the Mayor . . . .   *Rebecca Caudill* . . . 221
A Day in Mexico . . . . . .   *Belle Coates* 228
King of the Range . . . . .   *Margaret Jamison* . . 236
Singing Cloud . . . .   *Laura Adams Armer* . 244
A Rope Around the Sun . . .   *Indian Legend* . . . 251
Spotless Smith, the Cowboy . .   *Glen Rounds* 258
The Mischief Maker . . . . .   *Enid Johnson* 265
PHONICS 340
THINKING ACTIVITIES 352

West of the Rockies

Far-off Places . . . . . .   *Earl Marvin Rush* . . 274
The Wonderful Saw . . . . .   *Robert L. Grimes* . . 282
Holding Hands . . . .   *Lenore M. Link* . . . 290
Sandy Does the Wash . . .   *Neil Anderson* . . . 291
Little Pedro . . . .   *Joseph Longstreth* . . 299
The Princess on the Glass Hill . *Fairy Tale* 307
The Smoke Jumpers . . . . .   *Leland Silliman* . . . 315
From Coast to Coast . . . .   *Jack Bechdolt* . . . 323
PHONICS 343
THINKING ACTIVITIES 353

Take-off

Jim Hunter stood watching the airplanes take off and land.

"What a big airport this is!" he said to his father. "I guess it must be the best one in the state."

"It is, Jim," his father answered. "All the big planes that fly into our state land here. Look, there's one coming in now."

A large airplane landed on the far runway. Then it crossed the field and came to a stop near the fence where Jim and his father were standing.

"Is Uncle Jim's plane as big as that one?" Jim asked his father.

6

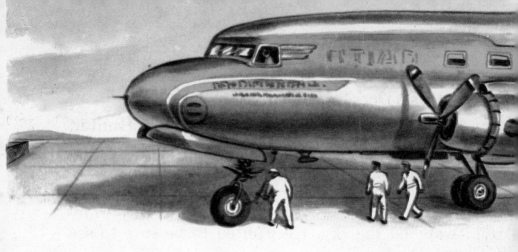

"Oh, no," answered Mr. Hunter. "He owns a very small plane—but a good one. He has been around the world in it."

"Around the world!" exclaimed Jim. "All by himself? That's something!"

"Yes, it is," said his father. "He really likes to fly. He has been more places than most people ever see as long as they live."

"But, why?" asked Jim. "Why does he travel all around the world the way he does?"

"He writes books, you know," answered Mr. Hunter. "He writes about the people he has met and about the places where they live. Maybe you would like to read some of his books. They're very interesting, I think."

"Is that all he does?" asked Jim. "Write books? Does he make any money?"

"Well, I guess he does!" said Mr. Hunter. "People say he writes the most interesting travel books they have ever read."

While he and his father were talking, Jim watched the sky. He wanted to be sure to see Uncle Jim's plane come in.

All at once men with cameras in their hands were standing near Jim and his father.

"Jim Hunter should be coming in soon," one of them said. "I hope he will have time to talk with us. His world trip will make a good news story."

"You're right," said another. "My paper wouldn't miss this story for anything."

Just then Jim saw a little red airplane come down at the far end of the field.

8

It was Uncle Jim! The newsmen got their cameras ready. A crowd of people now stood at the fence to get a better look.

"He must be a great man," said Jim.

"He is," said Mr. Hunter. "I'm proud to have an uncle like him. He's your great-uncle, you know. You were named for him."

Jim laughed. "With a name like his, maybe I can do great things, too."

That night at home Uncle Jim told about all the interesting places he had been. "But I'll tell you," he said. "I still think the United States is one of the most beautiful places in the world."

"Are you going to write a book about it?" Jim asked.

"You guessed it," laughed Uncle Jim. "To get my story, I'll fly cross-country from one end of the United States to the other. Look at this picture, Jim. It will give you an idea of all the places I will write about."

Pacific
Ocean

Mexico

10

Canada

Atlantic
Ocean

Gulf of Mexico

11

Jim laughed when he saw the picture his uncle showed him. "We're studying the United States in school this year," he said. "But we don't have pictures like this! Boats crossing the ocean! Cowboys and horses!"

"Just my idea of interesting people or beautiful places to see," Uncle Jim told him.

"I wish I could hop a ride with you," said Jim. "I've never seen the ocean. And imagine seeing cowboys and everything! That would be more fun than studying!"

"Don't get me wrong," laughed Uncle Jim. "I'll be studying in my way, too. I'm sorry you can't fly with me, Jim. But you can take the same trip and never leave this room."

Uncle Jim reached into his traveling bag and pulled out six books. "For armchair traveling," he said. "A book about every part of the country I shall see."

Jim picked up the nearest book. "By the Sea," he read. "Well, Uncle Jim, I'll be ready to take off whenever you are."

By the Sea

The Treasure Hunt

Polly and Joe Parker were playing that they were pirates. They had just brought their make-believe pirate ship into a harbor. Joe was still on board the ship, but Polly had jumped onto the sand.

Suddenly Polly called, "Joe, I've found something. I think it's a treasure!"

Joe ran to the spot where Polly was digging with her hands. The sand was flying in all directions.

"Look," said Polly, pointing to something dark in the sand. "I'm sure it's a treasure."

"Funny!" said Joe. "We never saw it before."

"It's treasure!" said Polly. "If we dig hard enough, we can get it out of the sand."

Soon Joe and Polly were both digging. They didn't get very far before a bell began to ring. The children listened.

"One, two, three, four," they counted.

"It's four bells," said Joe. "Supper time. Let's hurry. We can tell Grandfather about the treasure at supper."

The children ran over the sand to their grandfather's house near the ocean. Their grandfather was the captain of a fishing boat. Everyone called him Captain Tom.

Captain Tom had sailed the oceans of the world before returning to his home state of Maine. Now that he lived on land, he still did things the way a seaman does them.

The first summer the children had come to stay with Captain Tom, they learned to tell time the way the old sea captain did. On a ship at sea a bell rings every hour and every half hour.

Now Polly and Joe never said, "It's six o'clock." They said, "It's four bells."

Captain Tom was not only a good seaman, but he was a good cook, too. Tonight he had baked fish for supper. The children could smell it when they came into the kitchen.

"My, that fish smells good!" exclaimed Joe as they all sat down at the kitchen table.

"There's nothing like baked Maine fish," laughed Captain Tom. "Whenever I ate fish in far-off waters, I thought of our Maine fish."

"I'm glad we live in Maine," said Polly.

"Grandfather, shall we tell you a secret?" asked Joe. "We have found buried treasure! We shall need your shovel to dig it up."

"Buried treasure!" Captain Tom exclaimed.

"Yes, it's deep in the sand," said Polly.

"Maybe it's pirate treasure!" said Captain Tom. "Pirates used to like Maine. They used to sail their ships into our harbor and hide. Wherever they went, they used to hide their treasure, too. Maybe there's some buried close by. I think we should take a look. I'll go with you after supper."

The children never ate so fast!

"I think we have found an old chest buried by the pirates," said Joe.

"Maybe the old chest is filled with gold and beautiful jewels!" Polly exclaimed.

"We shall soon find out what the pirates buried in it," said Captain Tom.

The treasure hunt began right after supper. Captain Tom took his shovel with him. Soon they reached the spot near the ocean where the chest lay buried in the sand.

"It does look like something pirates would hide," said Captain Tom with a smile.

Then they all took turns shoveling. How the sand did fly!

17

At last they got to the chest, deep in the sand. There was a heavy chain around it with a big lock. But the key was in the lock, and Joe was able to turn it.

He opened the lock. Then he took off the chain and opened the chest. There were pieces of glittering gold—money, watches, gold rings, and jeweled chains!

Joe picked up a piece of the gold money. It wasn't very hard. He looked more closely. Then he saw it was a piece of candy covered with glittering gold paper.

Polly picked up a ring and a jeweled chain. She could tell they were not real, but they were pretty. The children looked at Captain Tom with questioning eyes.

He smiled at Polly and Joe. At last he said, "There is an old saying that all is not gold that glitters! But maybe there's more treasure in the chest."

The children looked deeper into the chest. They found two bundles. One bundle was marked "Polly." The other bundle was marked "Joe."

In each bundle was a child's raincoat and rain hat. They were like the big yellow rain clothes that fishermen wear on stormy days.

The children tried on their hats, which were just right. Then they looked at their raincoats. In each raincoat was a book. Polly's book was *The Blue Fairy Book.* Joe's book was *How to Make Boats and Sail Them.*

"Oh, I love our treasure!" Polly exclaimed. "It wouldn't do for a pirate, but it's just right for us!"

"Yes, it's real treasure!" said Captain Tom.

What Do You Think? Solving problems

A ship's bell rings 8 times at the most—at 4, 8, and 12 o'clock. How many bells for 6:00? 4:30? 8:00?

Little Whitetail

"I'm big, so big
That I can go
To eat by the pond
Alone! Oh! Oh!"
sang Whitetail.

The little deer was called Whitetail because his funny short tail was white. The rest of his coat, which had been almost red, had turned to brown. By now his sides had lost their creamy white spots.

The little deer's mother listened to him.

When he finished singing, she said, "No, Whitetail, you must learn more before you go to the pond. Remember, not all the animals in the woods are friendly."

But Whitetail sang on,

"I'm light on my feet.
Just wait. You will see
How fast I can run.
They can't catch me."

Away leaped the little deer, over the grassy hills! All the while his white tail was pointed straight into the air.

"Yes, you're a fine leaper," his mother said when he returned. "But what would you do if you met a bear?"

"I would leap straight home," he laughed.

"But bears can run fast, too," said his mother. "You must stay near home and play with your brother. Wait until the moon is big and round. Then I'll take you both to the pond to eat water plants."

21

When the mother deer walked off into the woods, Whitetail and his brother took turns leaping over each other. They often played this leaping game together.

But soon Whitetail began to think of the plants that grew by the edge of the pond. How his mouth watered! He was finding it hard to wait for the big moon.

Then Whitetail sang to his twin brother,

"Brown Eyes! Brown Eyes!

Listen to me.

I'm off to the pond.

DO come with me."

"Hasn't our mother often warned us not to go alone to the pond?" Brother Brown Eyes asked. "Wait until Mother takes us."

But Whitetail decided to go alone.

As he leaped through the pine woods, he met a gray squirrel. The gray squirrel warned him,

> "Never, never
> Would I go
> Off by myself.
> Oh, no! No! No!"

But Whitetail only laughed at the squirrel's warning and ran on.

Soon he reached the edge of the glittering pond. He buried his face in the wonderful water plants.

As he was eating the plants, an old crow in a tree warned him,

> "Little deer,
> How I do fear
> Something will happen
> If you stay here."

But Whitetail was having so much fun, he did not listen to the crow's warning. He went on eating at the water's edge. He did not believe there was anything to fear.

Suddenly he heard a strange sound. His nose caught a strange smell. He looked up. Straight ahead of him he saw the hungry eyes of a fox!

Whitetail knew a fox was more to be feared than a bear. He was so afraid that for a minute he could not move. He felt chained to the spot. He could not think.

But suddenly he leaped into the pond and swam toward the other side. As he swam, he called to his mother, but she was too far away to hear him.

At last he reached the other side of the pond. He climbed onto the land, thinking he was safe.

But there were those glittering eyes again. The clever fox had run around the pond!

The fox was ready to spring on the little deer. In a flash, Whitetail remembered the leaping game he had often played with his brother. Would it work on the fox? He would try it!

One, two, three, and he leaped. He leaped straight over the body of the fox. Then he ran toward home.

The fox chased Whitetail, but he could not catch him. Soon the little deer was safe with his mother.

"I'm proud of you," his mother said. "But now will you promise me not to go to the pond alone until you're older?"

"I promise," said Whitetail.

He kept his promise. He kept close to his mother and his brother.

His mother kept her promise, too. One night when the moon was big and round, she took Whitetail and his brother to the pond. And how wonderful were those water plants!

What Do You Think?   Locating information; Drawing conclusions

When Whitetail was younger, he had white ____ .
   tail   face   spots
Whitetail was safe because he knew how to ____ .
   sing   leap   hide

The King of Smithland

Once upon a time there was a king who lived with his queen in a funny kind of land called Smithland.

The king's name was Bozo, and the queen's name was Alice. They had only one child, Prince Peter.

Smithland once had a much longer name that nobody was able to say. The king himself tried and tried to say it, but he never could.

One day the queen's mother, Mrs. Smith, had an idea. She insisted that the name of the country should be changed.

"Nobody can say the name of this land," she said. "So you should give it a short name."

"I guess you're right," said the king.

"I should be pleased if you would call it Smithland," said Mrs. Smith. "After me!"

"Smithland!" said the king. "A good name! I shall insist that everyone drop the old name at once."

So the king ordered the sign at the railroad station changed to Smithland.

He ordered new writing paper for the castle. He sat down at once to write to all his friends, "Having a wonderful time. Wish you were here."

His friends thought he was on a trip until they heard that the name of his country had been changed.

King Bozo loved sitting on the roof of his castle. He loved watching his people through field glasses, a present from Queen Alice.

Every day he would go up to the roof of the castle and look through the glasses for hours and hours. He wanted to see if his people were doing anything wrong.

He had made lots of laws. Anybody who did wrong had to pay a fine.

Sometimes King Bozo would see the people doing something that he didn't like. If there wasn't a law against it, he would do something at once. He would march downstairs, get out his writing paper, and write a new law.

Once the king looked so hard through his glasses that he almost fell to the street. He was glad he didn't fall, because he had made a law against dropping things on the sidewalk.

The king took in lots of money from his fines. The first fine was never more than half a dollar. After that the fines became higher and higher. Sometimes they were as much as fifty dollars.

So only rich people had money enough to do wrong. It was a game with them. They tried to see who could pay the highest fines.

In some lands people talk about their big cars or their big houses. In Smithland people talked about their big fines.

But after a while the people grew tired of being watched. They no longer felt free to do as they pleased. So they put heavy curtains on their windows. King Bozo became very angry at this and made a law against curtains. All the time he kept on looking through his field glasses.

As time went on, King Bozo grew more and more interested in what happened within his country. He began to study lip reading. By watching people's mouths, he could read lips and tell what they were saying. In that way he missed nothing that was said. So people were not free to say what they thought.

Now in Smithland there was a little girl named Jenny Green. Jenny liked to climb trees to watch the birds and the bees. But the king had passed a law saying that girls couldn't climb trees.

Jenny became very angry when she heard about this law. She had to give up climbing trees, for her mother was poor and could not pay fines. So now Jenny had to watch the birds and the bees from the ground.

One lovely spring morning King Bozo went up to his roof. He looked through his glasses at all the people passing by. As far as he could see, they were doing no wrong. Then he saw Jenny!

Jenny was sitting under a flowering apple tree, watching the robins and bees in the treetop. But poor Jenny could only sit. She sat very still, but her lips kept moving. She was saying something strange.

The king tried to read her lips. He became very angry when he couldn't make out what she was saying. At last he gave up and went back to his rooms within the castle.

King Bozo could not sleep that night. All he could think about was Jenny. He could not get her out of his mind. Why couldn't he read her lips? What was she saying?

When morning came, King Bozo rushed to his roof again. Up went his field glasses! There was Jenny sitting under the tree. She sat very still, but her lips kept moving.

Again King Bozo could not read Jenny's lips. So he sent for her. He insisted that Jenny repeat what she had said.

Jenny was glad to repeat it. "The-a-bee king-a-bee is-a-bee an-a-bee old-a-bee busy-bee body-bee," she said.

She did not mind repeating it again. Still King Bozo could not tell what she said.

He sent for Queen Alice.

Then Jenny repeated to Queen Alice what she had said. The queen could tell what Jenny was saying.

The queen told King Bozo and he said, "Maybe it's true."

Then and there he ordered his field glasses broken.

As for Jenny, everybody in the castle liked her. And when she grew up, Prince Peter asked her to be his wife.

She made a wonderful queen. The people of Smithland loved her and had a pet name for her. They called her Queen Jenny-bee.

How the Bridge Helped

Jane and Pat Warner lived in a little white house close to the river's edge. They lived not far from the spot where the river ran into the big lake.

Mr. Warner was a fisherman who owned a fish store in Rivertown, too. As he was out all day fishing, Mrs. Warner ran the store. Sometimes Jane and Pat helped their mother.

One morning Jane said to Pat, "Mother's birthday is coming soon. Let's buy her a new jacket. Her old jacket is all patched."

"All right," said Pat. "Let's look in the Wish Book and see what we can find."

As soon as their mother went to the store, the children looked in the big order book. It was filled with colorful pictures of many things that would make wonderful gifts.

After they had looked through the parts that showed coats, dresses, and hats, they came to the jackets. At last they found a picture of the very jacket they wanted.

They made up their minds to get this gift for their mother. But they would have to pay seven dollars and fifty cents for it. In their two small banks they had only six dollars and fifty cents.

"Do you think we could earn the rest?" Jane asked Pat.

"Maybe we could earn some of the money by working for Captain Peters," said Pat. "He might pay us a few cents an hour."

Captain Peters was master of the large bridge which stood where the lake and the river met. He always welcomed Jane and Pat whenever they came to see him.

The children climbed into their own small boat and began to row toward the bridge. They went everywhere in their rowboat. Most often they went to the bridge. They thought it was the most beautiful bridge in the world.

The bridge went from the east bank of the river to the west bank. Day and night many cars traveled over the bridge because it was part of a great highway. At night the lights on the cars glittered like jewels.

Captain Peters lived in one of the twin towers that stood on the west end of the bridge. He lived there with his yellow cat named Prince.

The children found Captain Peters in his tower, watering a row of flowers in his window. Prince sat on a soft chair nearby.

When Prince saw the children, he jumped down from the chair and walked over to them. He remembered they always brought him fish to eat. Today they had brought three small fish for him.

Then Jane said to Captain Peters, "Have you any work for us? We will dust your apartment for ten cents an hour."

"That's an interesting offer," said the captain. "But we get our dusting free."

The children looked so sad that Captain Peters went on to say, "I'll tell you how it is. When my place is dusty, I just open a window on each side of my tower. Then the wind blows out every tiny piece of dust."

Suddenly Jane had another idea. "Could we wash your plates?" she asked him in a hopeful voice.

"Thanks for your offer," laughed the captain. "But Prince washes his plate, and I wash my plate."

The children did not tell the captain they needed to earn money to buy a jacket for their mother. They just said good-by and went down to their rowboat.

"What do we do next?" asked Pat.

Then they heard the deep whistle of a big boat, asking for the bridge to be lifted.

A big boat could not pass from the river into the lake if the bridge did not open. The bridge was lifted by a motor in one of the twin towers.

The children heard the bell ringing on the bridge. All cars had to stop. Then the motor began to lift the bridge. Up went the large gray bridge. Then the big boat passed through and into the lake.

But why was the bridge staying up? It should be going down by this time.

"The motor must be broken!" said Pat. "Captain Peters will have to telephone for a repair man."

In about ten minutes the repair man rushed along the east bank of the river. He had to cross the river to the west bank.

Pat offered to row him across.

The repair man called out, "Thanks! I was wondering how I could cross the river to repair the motor. Will you please be quick?"

The children rowed the repair man across the river as quickly as they could. All the while the captain watched and waited in the tower. When they reached the west bank, the repair man jumped out.

He surprised the children by handing each of them ten cents. Then he rushed up to the motor tower.

The people soon learned that it would take two hours to repair the motor.

Most of the people left their cars and went down to the banks of the river. They kept looking at the children's boat.

Then one man said, "Our baby is hungry. We are, too. How much would you want to row us across the river to an eating place?"

"Ten cents each, round trip," said Pat.

"The baby can ride free," said Jane.

It took three trips to row all the people across to an eating place. Then the children had to row all of them back. The last trip was made just as the motor began to work again. Down went the bridge. And across went the people in their cars.

Pat and Jane were tired but happy.

"That was hard work!" said Jane. "But I didn't mind. We can buy Mother's gift now."

What Do You Think?   Classification

One Name for All

Captains, fishermen, and repair men are all ____ .

Jackets, dresses, and coats are all ____ .

Seven, fifty, and ten are all ____ .

The Long Road to Rivertown

"You're late with your turkeys this year," said a man fishing from the bridge.

"You're late," called a farmer.

Many times John repeated, "Yes, we are late. Our father wasn't well, so we couldn't start any sooner for the market."

John's father had said, "I hope you get our flock of turkeys to Rivertown before snowfall. I'm sorry I can't go myself, but I'm glad you are willing to make the trip."

All this happened long before there were trains or motor trucks. John and his sister Mary had to walk fifty miles to take their flock of turkeys to market. Before they left, their father gave them a map which showed good places to stop along the way.

The children walked down the long road to Rivertown, driving the turkeys ahead of them. Each child was carrying a switch with a few leaves on the end of it. They used the switches to keep the flock together, but they used them lightly.

On his back John was carrying a bundle of warm blankets. Mary had a basket of food over her arm.

From time to time, John looked at the map. "I believe we can make five miles a day," he said. "If we can, we shall reach Rivertown in ten days."

"I hope we can," said Mary. "We must get the turkeys to market before the snow falls."

The first day of the trip went very well. The turkeys walked along the edge of the road and ate insects.

Sometimes a turkey would leave the flock to chase an insect in a nearby field. Each time John or Mary would bring the turkey back into the flock with a light switching.

When evening came, the children looked at their map for a place to camp. Soon they found a good camping place on a fruit farm.

When the turkeys had gone to sleep in the trees, John and Mary ate food from their basket. Then they rolled up in their warm blankets and slept on the ground.

Almost a week passed in this way. The children found that they could walk five miles a day with the turkeys. Each night they camped on a fruit farm, and the turkeys slept in the trees.

Most of the time, the turkeys ate only insects. But sometimes John would buy feed for them as they passed through a village.

Then one night a heavy frost fell. After that, the days and nights grew colder.

The next day a dog ran out of a village and barked at the flock. One of the turkeys flew over a fence and out of sight.

John and Mary ran after him with their switches, but they could not find him.

"Never mind," said John. "We can't take time to look for him. The important thing is to get to market quickly, before it snows. It is almost time for the full moon. I'm sure the full moon will bring snow."

That night the children slept on some hay near the trees in which the turkeys slept. The hay and the blankets kept them warm and dry.

The following night the children slept in an empty ice house. The ice house was dry, so the children had a quiet, restful sleep.

The next night was very cold. A farmer's wife said to them, "What a sight you are! You are blue with cold. You must sleep in our house, where it's warm and dry. Your turkeys can sleep in our barn. Can't you stay a few days and get rested?"

John said, "No, thank you. We must not stay longer than one night. The air feels as if it's going to snow. Then we will never get our flock to market."

"Well, one quiet night indoors will not hurt you," said the farmer's wife with a smile.

In the morning John said to his sister, "Last night the moon had a large white ring around it. A ring like that means snow."

"Yes," said Mary quietly. "I can feel it in the air. That means we must reach Rivertown tonight. If we aren't there by evening, we can walk in the moonlight. We must keep going."

They walked all day and most of the night. It was four o'clock in the morning when they caught sight of their uncle's house at the edge of Rivertown.

Soon they were sleeping in warm beds. They opened their eyes late in the morning and saw the ground blanketed with snow.

"I took your turkeys to market for you," their uncle said. "Everybody was surprised to see them. No one has ever been able to drive a flock here so late in the year."

John asked, "Did you get much money?"

"The flock brought more money than they would have last week," answered their uncle. "Then the market was full of turkeys."

Their aunt said, "Before we take you home, we will show you the sights of our village. You have earned a good time."

Where did the children stay the first night?
Where did they sleep the last night before they reached Rivertown?

Let's Make Gus Smile

Many, many miles west of Rivertown are five lakes that are called the Great Lakes. There are many islands in the lakes, both large and small.

On one of the small islands was a peach farm. And on this peach farm was a workman who never smiled. His name was Gus.

One summer Jane and Pat Warner went to stay with their aunt and uncle, who owned the peach farm on the island.

The children met Gus as soon as they got off the train.

"Who's that?" asked Pat when he saw somebody in Uncle Freddie's car.

"That's Gus," smiled Aunt Betty.

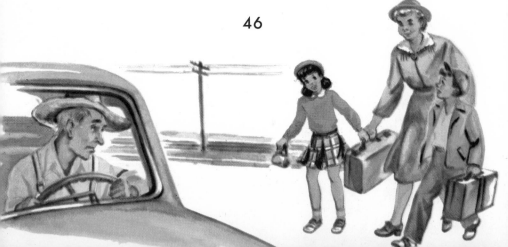

Gus was a tall, sad-looking man with a mouth that turned down at each corner. He looked as if he had never smiled in all his life.

"What a beautiful island!" said Jane. "The air feels so good!"

"The wind is bad in winter," said Gus.

Pat looked at the lake.

"I see a big white boat!" he exclaimed.

"The boats come too close," said Gus. "Something bad will happen some day."

"Where are the peach trees?" asked Jane.

"There they are," said Gus, pointing his thumb toward the long rows of peach trees.

Jane looked at the long rows of trees. "What beautiful peaches!" she exclaimed.

"They aren't ripe," said Gus. "They will not be ripe for three or four days. One bad storm could spoil them all."

Gus pointed his thumb at the sky. The sun was bright, and the sky was blue. But Gus looked as if a very bad storm might blow up at any minute.

"Peach farming is a hard life," he said. "The peaches will spoil. There aren't any pickers this year."

That night Pat and Jane invented the game called "Let's Make Gus Smile."

In the morning the children played the game they had invented. They told Gus their best jokes, but they just could not make him smile.

Later that day, the children walked around the island. They went up the country road and soon reached the village. On the edge of the village stood a small white house.

There were children in the yard.

"Maybe one of them knows a joke that will make Gus smile," said Pat.

Just then a playful puppy climbed through a hole in the fence and ran up the road.

Jane and Pat caught him and took him to the house.

"Your mother had better lock this puppy up or chain him," Pat told a pair of twins.

The twins took their thumbs out of their mouths and shook their heads.

"Our mother has gone away," they said.

A tall man holding a baby said, "That's true. The mother of our house will not be back until later this week. Thank you for catching the puppy. Will you come in?"

"We don't have time today," said Jane. "But could you tell us any good jokes to make Gus smile?"

The man shook his head. "Not offhand. But tonight, after all my children have gone to bed, I might think of something funny."

"We will come back tomorrow," promised Pat. "Then we will help you with the baby."

The children walked on until they came to a big building in the village. From that building came a very strange noise.

"I wonder what's the matter," said Jane. "Let's see what's going on in there."

They looked through the door and saw some people on roller skates.

"Would you like to skate?" asked a fat, red-faced man at the ticket office.

"No," said Jane. "We will just watch."

50

Then the man said, "Would you take tickets for a few minutes? I must get my shoes from the shoemaker across the street."

After the ticket man had gone, Pat and Jane took the tickets. They watched the people as they skated. One boy tried to invent a new way to skate. He fell down, and five people fell on top of him.

When Pat and Jane returned to the farm, they told Gus everything that had happened. No matter what they said, Gus never smiled. He just shook his head and looked sad.

"Our peach crop will be ripe in three days," he said. "But there will not be any pickers. The crop will spoil."

That night Jane said to Pat, "Pickers are the only ones who can make Gus smile."

"You're right," said Pat. "Tomorrow we must try to find some pickers."

All the next day the children looked for people to help. No matter where they went, everyone was too busy with his own crops.

On the third day they went to help the tall man with all the children.

"Where were you yesterday?" he asked.

"We were trying to find some pickers," Jane answered. "The peach crop will spoil if it isn't picked tomorrow."

On the way home, Jane and Pat met the roller-skate man.

"Where were you yesterday?" he asked.

"We were trying to find pickers yesterday, but everyone is too busy," said Pat.

The roller-skate man shook his head.

Early the next morning, Jane and Pat heard someone laughing in the yard.

"It's Gus!" said Jane as they ran out.

With Gus were the roller-skate man and some of his friends. The tall man and every one of his children were there, too.

They said, "We have come to pick! When people help us, we help them in return."

Gus didn't say anything. He was laughing for the first time in his life.

52

Study Pages

Vowel Sounds in Syllables

State the rule for each vowel sound and say the sound.

1. sand, chest, ship, fox, dust
2. wait, leap, goat, green
3. state, side, hope, use

Decide how many syllables each word below has. Count the number of places that have sounded vowels. Remember to count as a syllable:

y after a syllable, as in **windy**

le after a consonant, as in **table**

ed after **t** or **d,** as in **planted** and **handed**

end	body	insect	repeat
sang	straight	invent	insisted
lock	hide	skates	bundle

Which is an insect?

bee   squirrel   blackbird

Which is a part of the body?

voice   chest   life

What is made into a bundle?

sand   turkeys   blankets

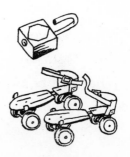

Strong Syllables

Say the word **promise** and listen to its syllables. What is the first syllable?

The first syllable **prom** is said with a stronger voice than the last syllable. It is the accented syllable.

Say the word **become** and listen for its accented syllable. The last syllable is stronger, or accented.

Now say these words and listen for the accented syllables:

against	village	market	lifted
ticket	repair	often	motor
shovel	turkey	castle	jacket

The ____ syllable of most words is accented.

    first   second   third

What can be lifted by a man?
ticket   castle   village

What can you buy in a market?
tower   turkey   bank

What can be repaired?
ocean   motor   tomorrow

What Makes a Joke?

Teacher: Jim, tell me where the Red Sea is.

Jim: Sure, Miss Lakewood. It's on that test paper you returned to me yesterday.

In the above joke, the teacher was thinking of a sea as a body of water. Jim, however, was thinking of the letter C.

Alice: I left my watch upstairs.

Jane: Won't it run down?

Alice: No, we have winding stairs.

Which two words have different meanings?

watch   left   run   winding

Captain: Well, we're half a mile from land.

Man on the ship: I don't see any land.

Captain: I mean straight down.

Which word has two different meanings?

from   land   see   mean

Tom: My father can hold up a car with one hand.

Jenny: My, he must be very strong.

Tom: No, he's a policeman.

Which words have two different meanings?

hold up   a car   very strong

Using What You Know

You know these rules:

1. One vowel sound, as in **at, set, it, not, cut**
2. Two letters side by side, as in **team, coat, train, need**
3. One sounded vowel letter and silent **e** as in **bake, side, nose, use**

The above rules are used to help you with the vowels in accented syllables.

Decide how many syllables each word has and which one may be accented. Then decide which rule will help you.

New Words

knife	robber	between	amuse
cabin	meat	shone	arrive
moaning	bite	tunnel	escape

Which ideas go together?

meat	cattle	robber
cabin	tunnel	hole
shone	escape	catch
cabin	home	bite
because	between	beyond
arrive	arrow	leave

Our Southland

A Train Ghost

Mr. Hunter looked at the train timetable. "George and Peter can take the early train," he said. "It leaves at nine o'clock in the morning. It reaches Grassy Point at six o'clock in the evening."

George said, "Grandmother promised to drive us to the farm in the station wagon."

"That means we shall get to the farm in time for the Halloween party!" exclaimed Peter.

"I'm glad you boys are going to visit Grandmother," said Mrs. Hunter. "You have never visited the South. And a Halloween party at your grandmother's house is fun. Maybe you will see the ghost."

"Oh, Mother," laughed Peter. "Is it true that Grandmother's house has a ghost in it?"

"Have you ever seen it?" asked George.

"Oh, yes!" smiled his mother. "Always on Halloween. Maybe you will see it this year."

54

The day for the long trip came at last. Mrs. Hunter took George and Peter to the railroad station. She helped them buy their tickets and find seats on the train. Then she spoke to a man in a dark blue suit.

"Oh, Conductor," she said. "My two boys are going as far as Grassy Point. Will you please keep an eye on them?"

"I keep an eye on all my passengers," answered the conductor with a jolly laugh.

George and Peter had visited many places in the family car, but they had never been anywhere on a train. They loved sitting in the long passenger car. It was fun to watch the people in the rows of seats.

"They're all going places," said George.

"So are we," laughed Peter.

During the morning the conductor spoke to the boys many times.

"We're going to our grandmother's house for a Halloween party tonight," they said. "Maybe we will see a real ghost."

The jolly conductor laughed as he went on.

At noon a man in a white coat walked through the passenger cars, ringing a bell.

"First call for lunch!" he said. "The dining car is three cars ahead."

George and Peter went into the dining car and took seats at one of the tables.

Then they ordered turkey, peach ice cream, and plum pie. This was very different from the kind of lunch they had at home.

56

After lunch the boys returned to the passenger car. During the afternoon they took turns sitting by the window. Every minute there was something different to see.

"We're moving right along," said Peter, looking at his watch.

But at four o'clock the train stopped suddenly. No one knew what had happened until the conductor came into the car. He stopped and spoke to the passengers.

"A milk train went off the tracks ahead of us," he said. "Nobody was hurt, but it will take three or four hours to clear the tracks."

"Oh, no!" said the boys sadly. "We will be too late for the Halloween party!"

A man behind the boys spoke up.

"Boys, my name is Mr. Camp," he said. "I couldn't help hearing what the two of you said. Maybe we could have a Halloween party on this train."

"On the train?" Peter asked. "How could we do that?"

"Wait and see!" said Mr. Camp. He left the train and walked across a cornfield to a farmhouse. A little later, he returned with a big, fat pumpkin in his arms.

The idea of a party was good news to all the passengers. Everyone wanted to help. Someone hollowed out the pumpkin and cut a face in it. Some of the men went into the woods and gathered nuts for the party.

"Now we need Halloween caps," said Mr. Camp. He opened a leather bag that was full of brightly colored party favors.

"Mr. Camp, who are you?" asked George.

"I'm a traveling man," laughed Mr. Camp. "I go to every big city on the map. I try to get the shops to buy my paper caps and other party favors."

58

At six o'clock the cook walked through the cars, ringing his bell.

"Children," he called. "Will you do us the favor of stepping into the dining car?"

When the children gathered in the dining car, they saw a wonderful sight!

The big pumpkin was lighted with a candle. At each place was a yellow candle, together with a paper cap, a balloon, and other party favors.

There was pumpkin pie for everyone, and little baskets of nuts.

In the corner of the dining car the cook had fixed a place where the children could duck for apples.

"Three cheers for the cook! Three cheers for Mr. Camp!" shouted George.

Then Peter heard a moaning sound. He saw something white moving in the candlelight.

"A ghost!" exclaimed Peter. The ghost had hollow eyes and a deep, hollow voice. It moaned again as it came nearer. Its long white arms reached out toward the children.

"You're just someone in a sheet," insisted George, with fear in his eyes. "It IS a sheet."

"A sheet presented by the sleeping car," moaned the ghost in a hollow voice.

The children laughed as the ghost took off the sheet. "The conductor! Three cheers for the conductor!"

It was a wonderful party. No one wanted it to end, but at last the train reached Grassy Point. Grandmother was at the station.

"How good it is to see you!" she exclaimed. "But it's too bad you missed our party."

"We had one on the train," said George.

"With a ghost, too," laughed Peter.

The Tom Thumb Train

Many years ago someone invented an engine that was different. It was run by steam, like other engines of the time, but it could move from place to place.

When people heard about the new engine, they said, "Why not use it in place of horses on our railroads? Then we could travel faster."

The day came when the new steam engine was tested. People stood along the railroad track to watch. Before long, it was clear that the engine was too heavy! It could not pull cars up the steep hills or around turns.

Some people said, "We can still use horses to pull cars up the steep hills."

Others insisted, "If we put sails on the train, maybe the wind would drive it along."

Then a clever young man named Peter Cooper had an idea. He had invented many useful things. Now he was interested in railroads. He told the railroad men, "What you need is the right kind of engine."

"That's not news to us," they said.

"It must be a small steam engine," Mr. Cooper went on. "Small enough to climb the steepest hills."

"Where will we find this wonderful engine?" asked the railroad builders.

"I'll build it myself," said Mr. Cooper.

The railroad men did not think his idea was worth much.

Peter Cooper did not mind what they said. He started to build his engine.

Time passed, and at last Peter Cooper's engine was finished. Everyone came from miles around to look at the new steam engine. How the men and women laughed when they saw it!

They still did not think it was worth very much.

The engine was as tiny as the handcars that railroad workmen use today. Because it was so small, it was named *Tom Thumb,* after the tiny boy in the old story.

"Well, Mr. Cooper," laughed one of the men, "the name is a good one, anyway."

"The engine is a good one, too," answered Peter Cooper. "We shall test it tomorrow. I'll take thirty people for a ride. It will be a day to remember in history."

But there was no trip the next day. When the thirty men and women gathered at the railroad, they heard bad news. Something had happened to the steam engine.

During the night a robber had quietly gone into the barn where the engine was stored. In the morning some important parts of the engine were missing. Without them, the test run could not be made.

Peter Cooper lost no time hunting for the robber. He got new parts and repaired the engine in a week's time.

The thirty men and women again gathered at the railroad for the promised ride. This time the engine was ready.

The thirty passengers quickly found seats in an open car behind the puffing engine.

Peter Cooper and three railroad men stood on the tiny engine.

Everyone was excited and happy. They felt that this day would be a great day in history.

Mr. Cooper started the engine. The whistle blew. The bell began to ring. Live coals flew from the engine. Then the wheels of the *Tom Thumb* began to turn.

Everyone cheered and shouted. Men waved their tall hats. Women waved, too. Boys raced alongside the train but were soon left behind.

The *Tom Thumb* went puffing along the track. It did what no one had believed it could do. It climbed steep hills and went around turns in the tracks.

This *was* a great day in history. It became one of the greatest days in the history of the United States.

By noon the *Tom Thumb* reached the end of the tracks. Everyone was excited by the run that the tiny steam engine had made.

The passengers climbed out, and the train was made ready for the trip back. Soon a coach pulled by a gray horse came up the tracks, stopping near the *Tom Thumb*.

The coach driver waved to Mr. Cooper. "How about a race?" he shouted. "My horse and coach against your train!"

"A race it is!" Mr. Cooper called back. "May the *Tom Thumb* win!"

The excited passengers climbed back into the car. Mr. Cooper and the railroad men climbed onto the engine.

"Ready! Go!" shouted the driver.

The gray horse leaped ahead.

The *Tom Thumb* was slow in starting. But as the coals grew hot, the wheels turned faster and faster. Soon the *Tom Thumb* caught up with the coach. Then the puffing little engine rushed ahead.

The railroad men shouted, "We will win! Mr. Cooper invented a wonderful engine!"

Mr. Cooper answered with a smile, "This is the end of horse travel. Steam is king."

Then the *Tom Thumb* began to go slower. Soon it stopped. A piece of leather had come off an engine part. The horse and the coach leaped ahead. The *Tom Thumb* passengers looked sad. They had lost the race.

But in days to come, the steam engine did win over horses. Mr. Cooper and the *Tom Thumb* showed that a steam engine could be used on a railroad.

Now history books call the *Tom Thumb* the "father" of railroad engines in our country.

What Do You Think?   Main idea; Relevancy

Find the key idea of the story. Then find another idea in the story, but not the key.

The *Tom Thumb* lost an exciting race.

Coal is found in the United States.

The *Tom Thumb* showed the world that steam engines were useful on railroads.

Something to Do

Mr. and Mrs. Bell lived alone in a tiny white house. All their children were big and had left home.

"I wish I had something to do!" Mr. Bell would sigh as he slowly rocked in his chair.

Mr. and Mrs. Bell lived in the warm South. They had orange trees in their yard, and there were two crops of oranges to be picked each year. However, between orange crops the Bells had nothing at all to do.

68

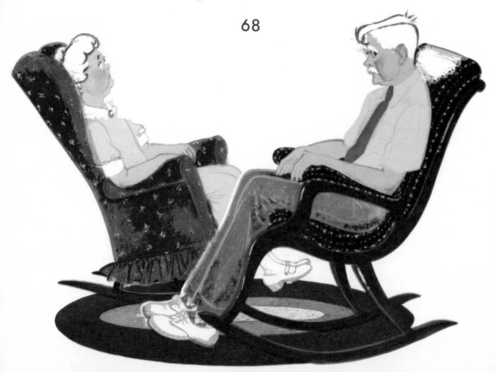

One day Mrs. Bell said, "I'll go to the pet shop and buy a kitten."

She came home with a little coal-black kitten that had green eyes and soft paws.

The Bells found a ball, some string, and other playthings for the kitten. They fed her some baby food and milk. They fixed a basket for a bed and made a beautiful pillow just for her.

The kitten was a very good little kitten. After she had been fed, she climbed up on Mrs. Bell's lap. As she grew sleepy, she put her nose between her paws.

"I wish I had something to do!" sighed Mrs. Bell while the kitten slept in her lap.

"I wish I did, too!" sighed Mr. Bell.

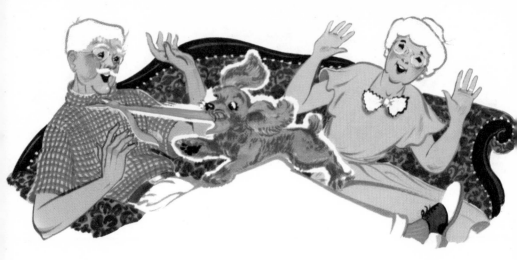

That evening the Bells heard something scratching at the door. When they opened the door, a puppy rushed in. She had long soft ears, big brown eyes, and paws that were too big.

"We must keep this puppy," said Mr. Bell. "She will give us something to do."

They made a pillow and put it into a box where the puppy could sleep. But the puppy climbed up on Mr. Bell's bed and began to cry. She kept on crying until Mr. Bell let her sleep on a pillow at the foot of his bed.

"Oh, well," said Mrs. Bell, "she's just a puppy. She's just like all puppies."

When the puppy was fed, she was not very orderly. She let her ears fall into the plate, and she spilled food on the floor.

When the puppy turned around, her tail fell into the food. As she tried to lap up milk, she knocked the plate over with her paws.

Mr. and Mrs. Bell spoiled the puppy. They had to pick up after her most of the time.

The puppy would often visit the neighbors. She would take newspapers from their front porches and bring them to Mr. Bell.

"Oh, well," said Mrs. Bell, "she's just a puppy. She's just like all puppies."

"Only more so," said Mr. Bell as he returned the newspapers to the neighbors.

The puppy chewed Mr. Bell's new shoes. She chewed the pillows and spilled their feathers all over the floor.

"Puppies will be puppies," said Mr. Bell. "She's just like all puppies."

"Only more so," said Mrs. Bell.

They named the puppy More-so.

"More-so is spoiled," said Mrs. Bell. "We must teach her to be good."

They taught her to be very good. They taught her not to spill the food or let her ears fall into it. They taught her not to chew the pillows or knock things over.

She slept in her box and left the cat alone.

"Between you and me, I think we taught More-so too much," sighed Mrs. Bell. "Now we have nothing to do."

One day More-so disappeared. The Bells hunted everywhere for her. They looked upstairs and down. They looked under the front porch to see if she were hiding there. They looked under the back porch, too.

She was nowhere to be found!

Mr. and Mrs. Bell sat with their hands in their laps. "We wish our dog had not disappeared," they said. They felt like crying.

One day they thought they heard a scratching at the door. That was More-so's way of knocking. They heard the scratching again, and they opened the door. They could not believe their eyes. In walked More-so with a tiny puppy in her mouth.

More-so placed the puppy at Mrs. Bell's feet. Then she disappeared and returned with a second puppy, and a third, and a fourth. Each one looked like More-so, only more so.

Mr. and Mrs. Bell said, "We'll name this one *Some,* and this one *Thing.* We'll name this one *To,* and this one *Do.* They must never be taught to be good. Then we'll always have Some Thing To Do."

What Do You Think?   Interpreting humor; Shifts of meaning

What's in a Name?
Why did the Bells call their dog More-So?
What did they call her puppies?
What will the Bells always have?

New Homes in Kentucky

Captain Boone and his party had traveled many miles through the woods to build new homes in Kentucky.

Now they stood on the top of a steep hill. Before them lay a rich, green valley. A winding river made its way through the fields.

"That's fine land, Daniel," said one of the men. "I wonder where we are."

Daniel Boone smiled. "That's the land we came to find," he said. "We're in Kentucky at last. We shall plant our crops and build our homes in this valley."

The people were happy to settle in the grass-covered valley. Soon a tiny village stood on the banks of the Kentucky River. High walls on all four sides made the village a strong fort.

Then one morning a man raced toward the village and shouted a warning. "Blackfish and his Indians are coming!"

The settlers rushed behind the walls of the fort and waited.

The following day, Blackfish and his Indians reached the fort.

"You must leave Kentucky," Blackfish told Daniel Boone. "We do not want settlers on our land. When will you be ready to go?"

"We shall give you your answer tomorrow evening," said Daniel Boone.

75

That night each settler was busy. Men repaired their guns. Women fixed food for them, enough to last many days.

When Blackfish returned, Boone said to him, "We have decided to stay in Kentucky. Your people and my people can live together on this land. There is more than enough in this rich valley for all of us."

Blackfish answered, "When settlers come, they always make the Indians leave their hunting grounds. But we do not want to fight. Give us your hands. We shall be friends."

Boone and the other men put down their guns and put out their hands.

At once the Indians leaped on the men and tried to pull them toward the woods.

But Boone and his men were able to get free. As they ran toward the fort, the Indians fired at them.

Inside the fort, men began firing, and the Indians ran for cover. Soon Boone and the others were safe behind the walls of the fort.

All that evening the Indians fired at the fort. During the night they went away, but they made a lot of noise as they left.

"They are trying to trick us," said Boone. "If they were leaving for good, they would go quietly. Blackfish wants us to fight outside the fort. He will lead his men back when he finds we are not following them."

Daniel Boone was right. In the morning the Indians returned quietly and began firing.

Late in the afternoon Daniel Boone called to his men. "Now we are in for it. I can hear the Indians digging a tunnel under the ground. When the tunnel reaches the fort, they will blow us up."

"What can we do?" asked the men.

"We must dig a tunnel that will lead into theirs," said Boone. "Maybe we can blow their tunnel up before they blow us up."

The men took their picks and shovels and started to dig. For days they worked as hard on their tunnel as the Indians did on theirs.

Then one night before the tunnel was finished, the settlers saw a strange sight. Burning arrows flashed through the air, and fell on the roofs within the fort.

"Now we are really in danger!" cried a settler. "The Indians will burn our fort to the ground. This is the end!"

"If it is, we'll go down fighting," shouted Boone as he climbed to a roof. "We must get the arrows off! Hurry! Hurry!"

The men rushed to help their leader. However, the arrows came so fast that soon all the roofs were on fire.

Suddenly a young girl cried, "Rain! I felt a drop of rain!"

The rain fell faster and faster on the burning roofs. Soon the fire went out, and the fort was saved.

But the danger was not over.

All during the next day it rained, but still the Indians worked in their tunnel.

During the night, the settlers could hear the Indians coming closer and closer.

"The Indians will be here in a few hours," a man warned. "They will surely blow us up tonight. Nothing can save us now."

Early in the morning the rain stopped. There was not a sound to be heard anywhere.

"I wonder what happened during the night," Boone said. "The Indians are very quiet. Not one of them is in sight."

"They are trying to trick us again," said one of the women.

The morning passed, and still there was no sign of the Indians.

At last Boone called a few men together. "Get your guns," he said. "We'll go out and see what the Indians are doing."

"Be careful!" a woman warned. "Don't let them trick you!"

Boone answered, "Have no fear! We'll be on the lookout."

Within an hour they raced back to the fort. "What about it, Boone?" a man called. "What has happened?"

"They're gone!" Daniel Boone shouted. "Every last one of them! The rain made their tunnel fall in. We are saved!"

The tired settlers cheered. Free from danger at last, they opened the heavy doors of the fort. Men, women, and children rushed out to thank their leader, Daniel Boone.

What Do You Think? Context clues (opposites)

Settlers left their <u>poor</u> farms for the ____ valleys of Kentucky. (new, rich, beautiful)

Daniel Boone was the kind of man others would <u>follow</u> if he would ____ them. (fight, save, lead)

Winter in the South

The South is not all just alike.
It has its north parts, too,
  Where snow may fall,
  Ice cover all,
As snow and ice will do.

But many children in the South
Have never seen the snow.
  An orange there,
  A flower fair,
Make winter a spring show.

And that's why people hurry south,
Why birds before the cold
  Go all a-wing
  Where they can sing
Through sunny days of gold.

Step-Along

The sun was going down in No-End Hollow as Nancy Burns started up the mountain toward home.

Nancy had been hunting all afternoon for many kinds of plant leaves. Her mother needed the leaves to make a spring tea.

Mrs. Burns always insisted, "Spring tea is good for people even if they aren't sick. Spring tea makes sick people well and well ones even better."

Mrs. Burns liked to gather her own plants, but today she had been too busy.

Nancy had twin brothers, but it was never safe to ask them to hunt for plant leaves. They could not keep their minds on plants. They might run off to hunt squirrels or woodchucks in the hills.

As Nancy climbed the steep trail toward home, the twins rushed up to her.

Teddy and Billy looked just alike. Even their voices were alike. "Guess what!" they cried.

"What trick have you thought of now?" asked Nancy.

"No tricks!" the twins insisted. "It's a surprise. Try to guess what it is."

"All right," said Nancy, "I guess chicken for supper."

"Yes," laughed the twins, "roast chicken! But you guessed only half the surprise."

"Half is about all I can do," said Nancy. "You will have to tell the rest."

"We have company!" said the twins.

"Company!" exclaimed Nancy. "Who?"

Just then Nancy caught sight of the cabin along the steep trail.

A peddler's wagon stood near the cabin.

"It's Step-Along, the peddler!" cried Nancy.

"He's going to stay all night!" said Teddy.

"Oh!" exclaimed Nancy. "Then he will show us all his things."

Step-Along always had a bag of treasures with him. Bright ribbons and dress goods— things a girl loved and wanted.

Whenever he finished showing the things in his peddler's bag, he would always say, "Well, I have to step along now." And that was how he got his name.

Nancy wished she could buy something from Step-Along. Then she remembered that the crops had been bad and there was little money in the cabin this year.

As she walked slowly up the trail toward home, she could smell the roasting chicken.

"We'll have a good supper, anyway," she thought. "A good company supper."

Now Nancy heard the peddler's voice. When she went into the cabin, she found him sitting in a corner with her father.

"Hello, Nancy," said Step-Along as he shook hands with her. "I hear your mother has taught you all she knows about plants."

Nancy smiled and went to help her mother. As she put the plates on the table, she could hear her father and Step-Along. They were laughing and telling stories.

At supper Step-Along began to sneeze.

"I crossed the brook yesterday, and I got my feet wet," he said. "Maybe I caught cold."

"Mother, let's make him some spring tea," said Nancy. She got out the big black kettle, filled it with water, and put in some leaves. Then she put the kettle on the chimney hook, above the fire. Soon the spring tea was steaming away.

When the tea was made, Nancy gave the peddler a long, hot drink of it.

"I'm glad you didn't try to go any farther tonight," she said. Her eyes were on the big bundle in the corner. She wondered if he was going to open it.

Just then the twins called, "Do you feel better, Step-Along? Will you please open your bundle?"

Step-Along sneezed. "Yes, I'll open my bundle," he said.

No one could help looking at all of the wonderful treasures. Wing ties, candles, ribbons, hooks and eyes, and a knife spilled out of the peddler's bundle. The twins looked with longing at the knife. Mrs. Burns liked the dress goods. And Nancy would have loved some bright red ribbons!

"Please close your bag," Mrs. Burns said. "We can't buy anything this year."

Before they went to bed, Mrs. Burns made everyone drink spring tea. In the morning everyone but the poor peddler felt fine.

Step-Along lay sick with a bad cold. He sneezed all the time, and his chest hurt. Nancy and Mrs. Burns took care of him all day. They made him drink lots of spring tea.

By evening the peddler felt almost well, and he ate supper with the others. They gave him the last piece of roast chicken—a wing. They always gave their company the best of everything.

After supper Mr. Burns took down his fiddle, which he always played for company. While he fiddled, the family sang. It was a fine evening.

"I feel a lot better," said Step-Along.

Next morning the sun was coming up over No-End Hollow as Step-Along got his wagon ready. His sneezes had stopped.

Mrs. Burns handed him some plant leaves. "The next time you sneeze, make some tea," she said. "Then you will not get sick."

"I promise to do that!" said the peddler. He opened his bag to put the leaves into it.

It seemed to Nancy that his hand stayed in the bag a long, long time. Then he pulled out a bright wing tie for Mr. Burns.

"For your fiddling that made me feel more happy!" he said.

Out came some flowered dress goods. "For making the tea," he said to Mrs. Burns.

Then came a jackknife for each of the boys. "Just for being twins," he smiled.

"And I know you picked the plants that made me well," he said to Nancy. "A bright red ribbon for each of your pigtails. Now, I'll have to step along."

"Thank you for the gifts!" everyone cried. Suddenly the cabin was filled with a happy feeling. As for Nancy, she could hardly wait to wear her new red ribbons.

A Tall Tale from the High Hills

My name is Dusty Banks. I am a tall man, and people say I tell the tallest tales in the South. But I say every word is true.

Things just happen to me. Listen to this story about the time I went to Boone Village. I wasn't looking for trouble. I just wanted to do a little shopping. Well, I want you to know that shopping got me in the most trouble you can imagine.

I was living on the other side of Bear Mountain, deep in the back woods. The trail from my cabin to Boone Village was long and winding, but my old pony and I knew it well.

In the fall of the year, I had a big crop of apples. When they were ripe, I tied two bags of them onto my pony's back. Then I took a switch to my pony and rode down the mountain to market them in Boone Village.

I reached the village safely, and I got good money for my load of apples. I had to buy some nails and a few other things.

"What can I buy for my wife?" I said to myself. "Maybe a kettle would please her."

Suddenly I remembered that the last time she ate meat was the time we had company visiting us. So I got her a pound of meat in the village store, loaded it onto my pony, and headed for home.

Now the trail over Bear Mountain is the steepest one around here. It goes through a hollow, through wild country all the way.

Suddenly my pony began to cut up. "Now what?" I said to myself. "There's trouble ahead, mark my words!"

The words had hardly left my lips when I saw a wildcat. And he wasn't in the bushes by the road. He was sitting in an oak tree over my head, ready to spring on me.

What claws that animal had! A man would be clawed to ribbons in five seconds. I tell you, no animal acts wilder than a wildcat.

Well, just as I caught sight of this one, I heard a roar from the other side of the trail. I looked! There in the bushes was the biggest, blackest bear I ever hope to see.

His eyes glittered with the meanest look I ever saw. He acted as if he would chew me up on the spot. His claws were like great hooks, and his roaring was enough to drive the daylight out of the valley.

The big bear roared again and leaped at me. At the same minute the wildcat opened his claws and leaped from the other side.

Well, I acted quickly. I ducked. My horse jumped to the side. Those two wild animals missed both of us.

I was running to escape when I heard fighting behind me. I looked back, and what did I see? The wildcat had landed head first right in that bear's open mouth! He was caught fast and couldn't escape.

Well, those two wild animals went right on fighting. They rolled over and over a hundred times or more. They scratched and clawed until they pounded the life out of each other.

So I loaded up! Now I had my meat, a wildcat, and five hundred pounds of bear. The biggest, blackest bear I ever saw.

You think this is a tall tale? Well, here are the fur cap, fur coat, and fur gloves my wife made me out of that wildcat's skin. There's a fine bearskin on our cabin floor, too. That's my story. Take it or leave it.

What Do You Think?   Fact and fantasy

True or Not?

A tall man could tell a tall tale.

A wildcat could spring from an oak tree.

A bear's roar could drive away daylight.

Dusty could load the two animals on his pony.

Bright-Eyes, the Little Raccoon

Bright-Eyes was a little raccoon who lived in the hollow of a live-oak tree.

Mother Raccoon was teaching her five babies to climb, but Bright-Eyes was afraid to try. He just couldn't climb all by himself!

Mother Raccoon called, "Mmmmmmm!" meaning "Come!" Then she showed him how to dig his claws into the bark of the tree. Holding him between her front paws, she took the skin of his neck in her teeth. She pushed his front paws a little way up the tree trunk. His back paws had to follow.

She kept his neck between her teeth as she pushed his front paws again. His back paws took another step. Bright-Eyes was climbing!

Soon Bright-Eyes was back in the tree with the other baby raccoons. They were settling down to go to sleep, for raccoons always sleep in the daytime. But today Bright-Eyes didn't feel like sleeping. The world about him was too interesting!

From the tree Bright-Eyes saw a neighbor family of opossums. The mother climbed along the trees that grew above the water. The baby opossums rode safely on her back.

The mother had a long thin tail that ran up and over her back. Each small opossum had his little thin tail hooked around hers. When the mother jumped from tree to tree, not one baby fell off into the water below.

"It must be lots of fun to ride that way," Bright-Eyes thought as he looked down.

Bright-Eyes crawled through the leaves of the tree to see more of the world. He saw something moving in the sand below. It was a big brown turtle digging a hole. She was going to lay her eggs in the warm ground.

Bright-Eyes was so interested in what was going on below he didn't remember to hold on to the tree. And thump! He took a spill!

Down he went into the swamp. He didn't like the swamp water, so he swam to the bank.

"Wa-a-ah!" Bright-Eyes cried. He was frightened to find himself so near the big turtle. He ran across the wet ground and crawled under some tall bushes to hide from the turtle.

High above, he could see the hollow in the tree where his home was. How he wished he were up there, safe and dry! But he couldn't climb the tree alone!

Here he was, getting deeper and deeper into the soft mud. There was no telling what dangers might be all about him.

Now he could see a bird with long, thin legs standing deep in the mud of the swamp. Suddenly a frog swam by. The big bird put his bill into the muddy swamp water. Up came his bill with the frog in it!

Poor little Bright-Eyes was frightened! He trembled and trembled. What if the bird should see him and want to eat him, too!

The sun shone red through the trees, and it was getting colder. It would soon be dark.

The tiny insects that filled the swamps began to bite Bright-Eyes. He tried to put his tail around his face to keep them away. Then he put his paws over his pointed nose so the insects wouldn't bite him.

Soon another frog leaped out of the water near the big bird. But the frog swam safely away because the bird was not quick enough.

Then the big bird looked into the tall grasses where Bright-Eyes had crawled. Had the bird heard him? Its black eyes were surely looking for him!

Bright-Eyes trembled with fear. He wanted to call for his mother, but if he did, the bird would hear him!

Suddenly Bright-Eyes heard a sound nearby. The bird heard it, too, and turned away from the little raccoon. Into the muddy swamp he went, after the frog that had leaped out of the water again.

Now Bright-Eyes could escape! He ran as fast as he could to the tree.

"Wa-a-ah!" Bright-Eyes cried. He was calling to his mother for help. He didn't know that his mother had missed him and was out trying to find him.

Bright-Eyes thought he heard the big bird right behind him. He pushed his front claws into the trunk of the tree. But he couldn't climb the tree all by himself! Not alone!

But then Bright-Eyes thought he felt his mother's teeth biting the back of his neck. She seemed to be pushing his front paws up the tree trunk. His back paws had to follow. Soon he had reached the hollow of the tree.

How happy Bright-Eyes was to be home! His eyes shone when he saw his brothers and sisters again.

The other baby raccoons were crying for their mother. Bright-Eyes wondered why they cried. Wasn't Mother Raccoon right behind him?

Bright-Eyes turned around to see his mother. But to his surprise she wasn't there! Where was she? Hadn't she just helped him climb up to the hollow of the tree?

And then suddenly Bright-Eyes knew what had happened. His mother hadn't helped him climb the tree at all! He just imagined that she was behind him, pushing him along. He had climbed the tree all alone.

In a short while Mother Raccoon did come home. How happy she was to see little Bright Eyes! She told him that she had looked everywhere for him.

Bright-Eyes told her of all the dangers he had faced. He told her about the big bird and how frightened he had been. He told her he had climbed the tree—all by himself. Mother Raccoon was so proud that her eyes shone. She knew that Bright-Eyes was growing up and could take care of himself.

What Do You Think?   Locating information (skimming)

Why could Bright-Eyes climb the tree alone?

The Story Teller

In a forest there lived a lion, king of all the animals. His word was the law of the forest.

"I like good stories," he said. "I want somebody to tell me one story after another without a break. He cannot stop. Each story must be better than the one before it. No two must be alike. I want to be amused."

The animals trembled at the order.

"Where is the story teller who can amuse King Lion?" said the rabbit to the squirrel.

"Where is the story teller who can amuse King Lion?" the bear asked the monkey.

The same question was repeated by the other animals. The deer asked it of the wolf, and the wolf asked it of the squirrel.

Even the largest animals of the forest trembled with fear.

At last the lion said, "If you can't find a story teller to amuse me, I'll roast all of you. But if you do find such a story teller, you will be safe. No harm will come to him or to any of you. I give you my word."

"We're lost," moaned the rabbit, the squirrel, and the monkey.

"Lost! Lost!" moaned the deer, the wolf, and the bear.

"Have no fear!" said the fox. "I shall save you from harm. I can tell many stories, each one better than the one before. Tell King Lion the story teller will soon arrive."

The animals hurried to tell the king. The fox brushed his fur, put on his finest coat, and arrived at the castle. His friends trembled as he walked into the room where the king sat on a soft pillow, switching his tail.

"Are you the story teller who can tell stories one after another?" asked the king.

"Such a one am I," said the fox.

"Then begin," said King Lion.

"Before I begin," said Mr. Fox, "I have a favor to ask. I should like you to explain what you mean by a story."

Mr. Fox had such a smile on his lips that the forest animals looked at him in wonder. Then the lion explained what a story is.

"A story is a story," he said, thumping his tail. "A story must tell something. It may be long or short. But it must tell an event. It must tell a fact."

"Very well," said Mr. Fox. "And do you feel that every story that tells a new fact or event is a new story?"

"I do," answered the king.

"Then I shall begin my tale," said Mr. Fox.

"Once upon a time a fisherman went to sea. He had a great net which he dropped into the waves. He caught many fish in the net. But as he pulled it in, he saw that some of the strings were breaking. Soon there was a hole in the net. One fish escaped."

At that point Mr. Fox stopped.

"What next?" asked King Lion.

"Then two fish escaped," said Mr. Fox.

"What next?" asked King Lion.

"Then three escaped," said Mr. Fox.

"What next?" shouted the lion.

"Then four escaped," said Mr. Fox.

As often as the lion repeated the question, the fox kept adding one to the number of fish that had escaped from the net.

At last the lion cried, "Enough! You're just adding numbers! Go on with the story!"

"I have told you thirty interesting stories," answered Mr. Fox. "Each of the thirty stories was better than the one that came before it."

"Explain that, please," roared the lion.

"Didn't you say that a new story is one which tells a new fact or a new event?" inquired the fox.

"I did," replied the lion, showing his teeth.

"And didn't you say it might be long or short?" inquired the fox.

"That's true," replied the king.

"I have told you many new facts or events," insisted the fox. "Isn't the escape of each fish from the net a different event? Isn't each event a different story?"

"How do you explain that each is better than the one before it?" asked the lion.

"Aren't two fish better than one?" inquired the fox with a smile. "Aren't ten fish better than nine?"

"You're right," replied the king. Then he added, "But I feel like dining on roast fox."

"Do not break your word," warned the fox.

"Even a king must keep his word," sighed the lion. He knew that he had lost. "I'll do you no harm."

Study Pages

How Many Syllables?

1. When **ed** is added to a word that ends with **d** or **t,** it makes another syllable, as in **landed** and **counted.**

2. The **e** is silent in words like **make, time,** and **nose.**

3. When the letter **r** is seen after vowel letters, the sound of **r** is heard with the vowels, as in **harm, roar, ear.**

Remember the three facts above when deciding the number of syllables in each word below. Count the number of places where you see vowels that may be sounded.

bite	because	glittering	opossum
roasted	frighten	wonderful	grandmother
apartment	hundred	peddler	important
visiting	insisted	passenger	sneeze

Which would you wish to have?

one hundred pennies   an important idea

an opossum   a glittering jewel

Unaccented Last Syllables

You know these unaccented last syllables:

LAST SYLLABLE	KEY WORD
y	body
ey	money
le	table
el	travel
er	darker
or	color
on	wagon
en	broken
in	robin
ow	yellow
et	blanket
es	switches

Now say each word below and listen for the last syllable. Decide which word above has the same last syllable.

favor	turtle	chicken	ribbon
arrow	ticket	valley	cabin
tunnel	matter	motor	pillow

Root Words and Changes

When endings **s** and **es** are added to some words, such as **claws** and **bushes,** you can see the root word **claw** in **claws** or **bush** in **bushes.**

Other words, however, have the root changed in some way before an ending is added. The root word **pony** has the **y** changed to **i** before **es.**

Below is a list of roots with different endings. Find each one that has a changed root word.

ROOT WORD	CHANGED WORD	KIND OF CHANGE
claw	claws	**+ s**
bush	bushes	**+ es**
pony	ponies	**y** to **i, + es**
add	added	**+ ed**
inquire	inquired	**+ d**
lap	lapped	**+ p + ed**
reply	replied	**y** to **i, + ed**
roar	roaring	**+ ing**
amuse	amusing	drop **e, + ing**
begin	beginning	**+ n + ing**

Which changed word tells:
what the child did who asked a question?
what the child did who answered the question?
what the hungry lion was doing?

Using What You Know

First, use the vowel sound of a word you know to say the accented syllable.

Then, use the unaccented syllable of a word you know to say the other syllable.

FIRST SYLLABLE	LAST SYLLABLE	NEW WORD
o in **not**	**on** of **wagon**	cotton
i in **sit**	**el** of **travel**	nickel
o in **not**	**et** of **market**	pocket
be of **before**	**o** in **strong**	belong
ee in **feet**	**y** of **body**	greedy
a of **about**	**a** in **same**	awake
a in **at**	**age** of **village**	baggage
a in **an**	**ic** of **magic**	attic

Which word means:

what is used to make clothes?

what a coat has?

what is needed for traveling?

a five-cent piece of money?

a room under the roof?

how you are after sleeping?

to be owned by?

River Days

Slow Poke

His real name was Joe Wentworth Fuller, but he was called Pokey because he moved so slowly. People thought he was a slow poke, for he never arrived anywhere on time.

It was not that he was really a slow poke. He could be as fast as anyone when he wanted. But he always found so many interesting things to see and do. The days were never long enough for him.

Pokey lived with his mother, father, and two older brothers in a cabin on a cotton farm. Around the cabin were cotton fields as far as he could see. But in front of the cabin was the Mississippi River.

As Pokey played by the river, he would lose all track of time. He would spend hours watching the boats on the river and the gulls flying overhead.

Pokey loved the Mississippi. He thought "Father of Waters" was a good name for it.

"It's the greatest river in the world," Pokey thought. "Anyway, it's the second largest. There's no other river where so many things can happen."

Then Pokey would hear a noise in the trees. Off he would go to follow the trail of a raccoon or an opossum.

Then he would return to the Mississippi and watch the boats, and the gulls overhead. Sometimes two gulls would fight over a fish from the river.

That was why Pokey was always late.

"Wait for me! Wait for me!" he was always calling.

One Saturday in early fall Pokey got up at daybreak.

"This is the day of the Cotton Picking Contest," Pokey thought to himself. "Today I'll be early. In fact, I'll be the very first passenger on the bus."

His older brother Freddie said to Pokey, "Here's a nickel for each of us to spend at the Cotton Picking Contest. One for you, one for Tom, and one for me. Don't lose your nickel. Put it in your pocket. And do hurry."

"I'm not going to lose this nickel," laughed Pokey. "It will be safe in the pocket of my overalls."

The Cotton Picking Contest was always the most exciting event of the year. It took place in a town called Greenbanks.

Greenbanks was thirty miles away, on the Mississippi River. The school bus would take the children there.

Cotton pickers from all over would be in the contest. The judges would watch each one. They would give the best man picker a prize of one thousand dollars.

The best woman picker would receive five hundred dollars. The best old man would receive one hundred dollars. Last of all, the judges would give a prize of fifty dollars to the best boy picker.

The contest would be like a fair, with bands and a parade. Almost a thousand people would flock there.

Pokey was ready to leave for the contest before his brothers. His face shone from all the washing he gave it. He had on his best blue overalls. In the top pocket was his nickel.

Pokey and his two brothers left the cabin early. They passed between the cotton rows leading to the highway. All they could talk about was what they would buy.

"I'm going to buy an orange pop with my nickel," said Freddie.

"I'll buy popcorn," said Tom.

"I'll buy an ice-cream pie," said Pokey.

Pokey put his hand inside his pocket. Where was his nickel? It had disappeared! It must have dropped out on the way to the road. He ran back and hunted in the dust.

"Hurry, Pokey," called Tom. "If you can't find your nickel, I'll give you half my popcorn."

"I'll give you half my orange pop," said Freddie. "But hurry. Here comes the bus."

Pokey saw them climbing on the yellow bus. "Wait for me!" he called.

But the bus was speeding up the road. Pokey's lips began to tremble. He was going to miss the contest.

Just then a neighbor, Mr. Hooker, pulled up in his truck.

"Hello!" he called. "Aren't you going to the contest?"

"I missed the bus," replied Pokey.

"Never mind," said Mr. Hooker. "I'll give you a lift."

Pokey hopped onto the truck. Soon they were speeding toward the fair grounds.

When they arrived, Mr. Hooker parked the truck. Inside a high fence was a field of cotton that had been planted for the contest. Crowds of people stood around the field.

"This is the largest crowd I've ever seen at the Cotton Picking Contest," said Pokey. "I don't see my brothers anywhere."

111

Then Mr. Hooker said, "Why don't you try for the boy picker's prize? Then your brothers will surely find you."

"Maybe I will!" Pokey said.

A few minutes later he found himself standing near a long row of cotton. Around his shoulder was a big bag.

Two hundred men, women, and boys were in the contest. Each had a row to pick. A gun went off for the contest to begin.

The pickers moved along the rows, putting the cotton into the bags on their shoulders.

"Pick it fast and pick it clean," Mr. Hooker shouted to Pokey.

Pokey picked all the ripe cotton he could see. He picked it clean, with no leaves.

Two hours rolled by. Then the gun was fired again. The contest was over.

Pokey and all the pickers took their bags to the judges' stand. They emptied the cotton onto the ground for the judges to see.

It seemed hours before the judges decided on the winners. A young farmer was called to receive the thousand-dollar prize. A housewife received the prize for women.

"Joe Wentworth Fuller!"

It took Pokey a minute to remember that was his full name. He couldn't believe it! He was a winner, too!

"It's not always speed that counts," a judge said to the crowd. "The kind of cotton that is picked counts, too. This boy picked the cleanest cotton." The judge gave Pokey a fifty-dollar bill!

Pokey's brothers ran up to him. "How are you going to spend your money?" they asked.

"I'll buy three orange pops, three bags of popcorn, and three ice-cream pies," said Pokey. "Then I'll begin saving to help pay for a cotton farm of my own."

The Bee Man

Out in the apple trees the bees sang softly. Frank Winters listened to them, for he felt that the bees were his friends. He felt that way because Mr. Cooper, who owned the bees, was his friend.

The house that stood nearby was very old. No one knew why Mr. Cooper had bought the old run-down place.

But Mr. Cooper knew why he had bought it. It was just the place for bees. The flowers of the old apple trees would make the finest kind of honey.

Mr. Cooper made hives—rows and rows of hives. Into the hives he emptied boxes and boxes of bees that he had bought.

Mr. Cooper told Frank all about his bees and how they make honey.

He said, "The best thing about bees is the way they take care of themselves. They wash their faces and wings. They keep their hives clean. They get their food in summer and sleep all winter. They really look after themselves. I wonder why more people don't like bees."

"People are afraid that bees will sting them," said Frank.

"If you rush up to them, they might sting you," said Mr. Cooper. "You have to come up to bees quietly. To be sure they don't sting me, I always wear a net."

Every evening after work Mr. Cooper sat in a chair near the old house. On his lap lay an old fiddle.

One summer evening when Frank visited Mr. Cooper, he inquired about the fiddle.

"Can you play any tunes?" Frank asked, looking at the fiddle on Mr. Cooper's lap.

"I just make sounds mostly," the bee man replied.

"Please play a tune for me!" said Frank.

"Listen to this," said Mr. Cooper.

The strings began to hum. They sounded like an insect humming nearby.

"That's better than a tune!" exclaimed Frank. "Can you make the sound of a bee?"

"Surely," the bee man answered. Again he played on his fiddle.

"Why, that sounds like an angry bee!" exclaimed Frank. "The way a bee sounds when it is going to sting you!"

"But my bees don't sting," said Mr. Cooper. "I'm careful not to frighten them, even when I take their honey or clean their hives. So my bees sound like this."

He played a quiet, humming tune.

"Can you imitate any other insects?" Frank asked. He wanted to hear more.

"Yes, I can," said Mr. Cooper. Then he imitated a pair of crickets.

"You can hear how differently Mr. and Mrs. Cricket sing," he said. "Her voice is high and thin. His voice is low and deep."

"I never knew that," said Frank.

Mr. Cooper explained, "Almost everything in this world, big or little, travels in pairs. Now take the tree frogs that make so much noise when it's going to rain. There's always a high, thin noise and a low, deep one."

The bee man imitated other insects. Frank had never heard such tunes.

"I believe people would pay money to hear those tunes!" he exclaimed.

117

"Oh, now, I wouldn't say that," Mr. Cooper replied. But he looked pleased.

Then he added in a low voice, "I could use a little money to fix up this old house."

That gave Frank an idea.

Frank's father worked for a television station. So Frank raced home to tell his father about his bright idea.

"Mr. Cooper can imitate real live insects on his fiddle!" he exclaimed. "Sometimes a tune sounds like angry bees. He can even imitate tree frogs, crickets, and everything! Father, why don't you put Mr. Cooper on one of your television shows? I know he would make a big hit!"

Frank was sure his friend would earn hundreds of dollars with his tunes.

"If you do Mr. Cooper this favor, he can really fix up his old house!" Frank went on. "And I can help him."

"Not so fast, Sonny," said his father. "But I would like to meet your bee man."

Frank took his father to meet the bee man and hear him imitate the insects. Mr. Winters was as delighted as Frank had been.

Within a week all the plans for the show were made. Mr. Cooper took his fiddle to the television station.

Mr. Cooper stood on the stage before a crowd of people. He was wearing his farm clothes and his bee hat with the net.

Frank stood proudly on the stage with Mr. Cooper. He asked him questions about his bees, just as he always did.

The bee man explained how bees take care of themselves. He told how friendly bees really are. Then he added that there is nothing better than honey on hot corn bread.

119

Mr. Cooper imitated angry bees getting ready to sting and quiet, busy ones. Then he asked the people what he was imitating.

The crowd kept him on the stage a long time. He imitated a pair of crickets and some frogs in a swamp. He imitated a hen scratching and a hummingbird at work.

Mr. Cooper and Frank turned out to be real showmen. Everyone was delighted with the act.

As Frank and Mr. Cooper were leaving the stage, a man rushed up. "I am glad to meet you," he said. "You are just the man who can help us sell more honey on a weekly television show."

Then and there he offered to sign Mr. Cooper and Frank for a ten-week show. How delighted they were with the plans!

Before long, Mr. Cooper taught Frank how to play the fiddle. The time came when Frank, too, could imitate bees, frogs, crickets, and even hummingbirds.

Pepperminta the Great

Pepperminta was a brown and white goat. She belonged to the Chickencooper family, who lived in a town called Peachland. Their house stood on Honeybee Street, between the library and the school.

From their dining-room window, the family could see across the schoolyard as far as the great Mississippi River. Mr. and Mrs. Chickencooper and their children liked to look out the window as they ate.

The Chickencoopers saw Pepperminta for the first time one frosty morning in early spring. At first they just saw something moving in the tall bushes by the river. Each one tried to guess what it might be.

There were six children in the family. The oldest was Daniel, and the youngest was Jimmy. In between were Bob, George, Patty, and Jane. All of them guessed.

"It's a steamboat," guessed Bob, "and it has been wrecked in the cattails."

"It's a sea lion," thought George.

"I believe it's a raccoon," said Daniel.

Patty hoped it might be a mother cat with six or seven kittens.

"I want it to be a cow that doesn't belong to anyone," said Jimmy. "Then we could keep her and have ice cream every day."

Their mother thought that it was a big turtle coming to lay its eggs in the wet mud. Their father decided it was just an opossum crawling through the bushes.

Jane looked very close. She noticed things that other people did not see.

"It's not a wreck or any of those things," she said as she hopped about like a cricket. "It's a goat! I've wanted a goat all my life."

The children left their breakfast and ran to see what it was.

They saw a small brown and white goat with a white star between its eyes. It was standing in the mud, eating its breakfast. It was chewing bushes as if they were soft cream puffs.

"A goat!" shouted all the children.

"You beautiful you!" laughed Jane. "How I love the star between your eyes!"

"We'll take this muddy goat home," said Daniel in the voice of an oldest child.

In a loving voice Jane added, "This sweet little goat will be so delighted to have a good home."

"What will we call her?" asked Bob.

"Pepperminta has a sweet sound, like candy," said Jane. "Pepperminta is so sweet. Let's call her Pepperminta."

But it was hard to get the sweet goat home. It took all six children, pulling and pushing hard, to get her there.

They put her inside the woodhouse and fed her a breakfast of corn and bananas. They even gave her a box of free dog food that had been left on the porch. Pepperminta was so hungry she ate all day long.

"She will eat us out of house and home," moaned Mrs. Chickencooper. "She belongs in a zoo—not here!"

"She may be lost," said Mr. Chickencooper in a hopeful voice. He put a notice in the morning newspaper, which read: "FOUND— one brown and white goat."

No one came for Pepperminta.

The Chickencoopers began to fear that Pepperminta would stay with them always. This thought frightened all of them but Jane.

Jane said, "Our sweet little goat is more wonderful than any animals I've seen at the zoo. I think she will be famous some day."

That afternoon Pepperminta got out of the woodhouse. When the family came home from a picture show, they found she had wrecked the front yard.

She had chewed all the grass, all the vines, and all the bark from the peach trees.

"And she is still so young," said Jane. "Think of the grass and vines and trees she will eat when she really grows up."

Mr. Chickencooper put another notice in the newspaper. It said: "WILL GIVE AWAY— one friendly, hard-working goat."

Only the secondhand peddler came to see about taking Pepperminta away. When the peddler saw what she had done to the yard, he decided he was too poor to keep a goat.

Mr. Chickencooper drove Pepperminta to the next town. He forgot to bring her home. But next morning a motor policeman drove up in a truck with Pepperminta inside.

"You forgot your goat," he said. "We found her yesterday in the next town. She was on the roof of a house, chewing the vines for breakfast. She has done enough harm. You should take her to a zoo."

But Jane cried, "You wait, Mr. Policeman. This goat will be famous some day."

While all this was happening in Peachland, other things were happening farther down the Mississippi River. Workmen were making plans to clear the swampland, thick with trees, vines, and bushes. They were so thick that not even a truck could tunnel its way through. The bushes must be thinned out.

One of the workmen said, "Goats can do it. Goats are light on their feet. They can move around in the mud. They will chew the thickest leaves and vines and bushes. Let's find goats to clear the swampland."

The workman drove all over the country, visiting people who had goats to sell. He bought hundreds and thousands of goats.

At last he saw Pepperminta. He was delighted! He asked the Chickencoopers to sell her on the spot.

"Pepperminta is a very sweet goat," cried Jane, "but sometimes she is a little greedy."

"Greedy goats are what I want," said the man. "They can't be too greedy."

He handed the Chickencoopers a ten-dollar bill and drove off with Pepperminta.

127

With their ten dollars the Chickencoopers bought seeds. Soon they had a street-side market, which earned money for them.

On Mrs. Chickencooper's birthday all the family went to a picture show. After the cowboy picture came the news. The news showed the work being done by thousands of goats to clear the swamplands.

One picture showed a brown and white goat with a white star between her eyes. She was chewing thicker vines and pulling up larger bushes than any other goat.

"Pepperminta!" cried the Chickencoopers.

And the voice from the sound track said, "Thousands of brave goats are saving our land. But no goat is doing finer work than this famous queen of the swamps."

"To think that our own little Pepperminta is now a great moving-picture star!" cried Mr. Chickencooper.

Jane exclaimed, "I always knew our sweet Pepperminta would be famous some day!"

Three Cheers! It's Spring!

"The rain is over!" cried Susan Towers. She sat up in bed and looked out the window. How bright the sun was today! It spilled gold over everything. And what a wonderful feeling there was in the air!

"Three cheers!" cried Susan. "It's spring!" She dressed and hurried to the kitchen where she found her grandmother cooking breakfast.

"Oh, Grandmother!" Susan cried. "Spring has come at last!" But then she noticed that her grandmother seemed troubled. Grandmother kept looking out of the window.

"Is something the matter?" Susan asked.

"Yes, Susan," answered her grandmother. "I'm happy that spring has come. But have you noticed how loud the river sounds? This is the time of the year for floods!"

After breakfast Susan always went to gather the eggs. Today the ground under her feet was soft and muddy. Sometimes her boots would slip, and she would almost fall down. After she gathered the eggs, Susan sat down on a box. She thought about home.

Susan's father was sick, and her mother was taking care of him in the city. Susan was visiting her grandmother. They were company for each other. But sometimes she got homesick so far away from her father and mother.

Grandmother lived alone on a farm near the Mississippi, where Susan's father grew up. He had told Susan about the floods on the great river. She half hoped her grandmother was wrong about a flood.

But still, a flood might be exciting.

The kitchen was warm from the fire in the coal stove. It felt very cozy and cheerful.

"Maybe we can see a show and stay in town overnight," said Grandmother.

At about ten o'clock Susan went out to the road to watch for the letter carrier.

When he drove up, he said, "You and your grandmother had better come to town with me. It looks as if we are going to have the worst flood in years."

"Grandmother and I are going to town this afternoon on the bus," Susan told him.

"I am glad to hear that," the letter carrier replied. "Now I don't have to worry about you. Oh, I almost forgot! I have a letter for you!"

The letter was from home. Susan's father was better, and she could go home next week.

"We'll get ready to go to town," said Grandmother. But before it was time for them to leave, the flood started!

Water rushed down the hills into the river, and soon the river was flowing over its banks. The overflow made a lake around the house.

Susan was frightened, and Grandmother looked worried.

"We must get busy," Grandmother said. "It looks like the worst flood in history."

First they carried some coal from the kitchen up to the attic.

"I don't want to burn up the chairs this time," Grandmother said. "That's how we kept the stove going in the last flood."

In the attic was a coal stove, as well as a bed and a table. Grandmother took pillows, blankets, a teakettle, and food up to the attic.

"We can be dry and cozy up here," she said.

Then they carried up some straw for the chickens. What a time they had getting the chickens themselves up to the attic!

The attic was cozy. But from the window, Susan noticed that the river was still overflowing. Flood waters were rushing along at greater speed than before. She could see boxes and trees and even the wreck of a trunk drifting by.

Early the next morning Susan and her grandmother heard a noise.

"It's a chair drifting against the walls of the room below," Grandmother said. "I am ready to give up. Leave some food and water for the chickens. We'll go when the boat comes."

"What boat do you mean?" asked Susan.

"During the floods the letter carrier sends a motorboat to pick me up," Grandmother said.

"Oh, dear!" cried Susan. "I told him we were going to town. Maybe nobody knows we are here. Maybe no one will send a boat."

Susan was really worried. She did not think the attic was cozy now. Even the chickens in the straw did not amuse her.

By breakfast time the next day there were two inches of water on the attic floor. Susan put on her boots and splashed around. But Grandmother shoveled more coal into the stove and started making cookies!

It seemed very funny to Susan. There was Grandmother in boots, standing in two inches of water, baking cookies! But Susan was afraid to laugh. She felt more like crying.

"We'll put a signal out the window," said Grandmother. "Someone will be sure to see it."

Grandmother found an old sheet, which she used for a signal. She tied the sheet to a board and put it out the window.

Now the water on the attic floor was four inches deep. Grandmother and Susan slipped and splashed around the attic and watched for a boat, but not one did they see.

They saw only boxes and boards drifting by the window.

Then early in the afternoon they heard an airplane fly over the house. They splashed and slipped over to the window where their signal was. They waved to the pilot and pointed to the sheet! Then the pilot landed his airplane on the water.

"Send a boat to get us out of here," called Grandmother to the pilot. "This is the first time a flood ever got the best of me!"

In no time a boat came up to the attic window. Grandmother and Susan crawled out the window into the boat.

By the time they arrived in town, all Susan's fears had disappeared. Her eyes shone because she was thinking of all the exciting events she could tell!

She wouldn't have missed the flood for anything. And she would always remember how Grandmother had made cookies during the worst flood in history!

Sleeping Beauty

"Hoo-hoo-hoo-hoo!" came the sound from up the river. All the children ran to the river bank, shouting, "The showboat is coming!"

Soon a large river boat pulled up to the landing. On one side of the boat was the sign "Stardust Marionette Company."

Some boys got off the showboat and passed out handbills, which read: "Tonight only! Stardust Marionette Company will present *Sleeping Beauty*. Marionettes as big as life. Buy your tickets early! Come one! Come all!"

That night the people bought tickets and flocked on board the showboat. They cheered when the stage curtains opened, and the show began.

136

ACT I

Place: A Castle

(The king and queen are sitting on golden chairs. Twelve good fairies come in.)

King: Welcome, fairies. We have asked you here to see our new baby, Princess Rose.

First Fairy: Let us all give her fairy presents.

(She waves her magic wand over the baby.)

First Fairy: You shall be very beautiful.

Second Fairy: You shall be as sweet as a rose.

Third Fairy: You shall have a lovely voice.

Fourth Fairy: Your eyes shall be as bright as jewels.

Another Fairy: You shall never be sick.

Another Fairy: You shall always be kind.

Another Fairy: You shall never be poor.

Another Fairy: You shall be as good as gold.

Another Fairy: You shall always be happy.

Another Fairy: Everyone will love you.

Another Fairy: You shall be a prince's wife.

Last Fairy: I cannot think of anything now. I shall give my present by and by.

King: We thank you. Now be seated. I shall pass the golden plates for the feast.

(The bad fairy walks in.)

Bad Fairy: What do you mean by having a feast and not asking me?

Queen: I would have asked you, but I have only twelve golden plates.

Bad Fairy: I am very angry. You will be sorry for this.

(She touches the baby with her magic wand.)

Bad Fairy: When the princess is fifteen years old, she will sit at a spinning wheel. Harm shall come to her.

The King, the Queen, and the Fairies: Oh, no! No!

Bad Fairy: Yes! Yes! When the princess is fifteen, she shall find a spinning wheel. The minute she touches it, she shall hurt her hand. Then she shall fall dead.

(The queen and all the fairies cry out.)

King: It must not happen!

(The bad fairy disappears.)

Last Fairy: Now I shall give my present. I cannot take the harmful wish away, but I can change it. The princess will be hurt, but she will not fall dead.

Queen: Kind fairy, what will happen?

Last Fairy: She will sleep for a hundred years. She will awake when a king's son shall come to the castle. Everyone in the castle will sleep, too, until she awakes.

All the Fairies: Good-by, King and Queen.

(The twelve fairies all go out.)

King: I will not let this happen. I shall make a law ordering that all the spinning wheels in the land be burned. Then the bad fairy's wish cannot come true.

ACT II

*(Fifteen years later. The kitchen
in the castle.)*

Kitchen Boy: Cook, what are you making?

Cook: A birthday cake for the princess. She's fifteen years old today.

Kitchen Boy: Is it true that she may hurt her hand on a spinning wheel? If she does, shall we all go to sleep for a hundred years?

Cook: Yes, but such a thing will not happen. All the spinning wheels in the land were burned long ago. Get to work, you lazy boy.

*(The king and queen are in the gold room.
Princess Rose comes in.)*

King and Queen: Happy Birthday, dear Rose.

(They give her a book as a birthday gift.)

(The bad fairy passes behind the family. She goes to the tower.)

Princess Rose: Mother, I think I heard someone going up the tower stairs.

Queen: It may have been the cat.

Princess Rose: I'll go see. I'll be right back.

(She goes to the tower and finds the bad fairy.)

Princess Rose: Oh! Who are you?

Bad Fairy: I am a fairy. I have a lovely birthday gift for you.

(She shows Princess Rose a spinning wheel. The princess sits down and starts to spin, hurting her hand as she does so.)

Princess Rose: Oh! Oh!

(She lies on a bed and goes to sleep. The king and queen go to sleep. The cook stops making cake and goes to sleep. The lazy kitchen boy goes to sleep, too. The bad fairy waves her magic wand over them.)

Bad Fairy: Sleep for a hundred years!

(She disappears.)

(In come twelve good fairies, dressed alike.)
The Good Fairies sing:
Where our fairy feet now fall
Grow big roses, strong and tall.
Hide from all below the skies
Where the Sleeping Beauty lies.
Bush, grow high. And vines, grow deep.
Let no one disturb her sleep.

ACT III

(One hundred years later. The castle has not been disturbed. The stone wall is covered with rosebushes. A young prince comes in.)
Prince: How high the rosebushes are! How thick upon the castle wall! But I'll crawl through them even if they tear my clothes!
(He cuts a hole in the bushes and crawls through them. They tear only his coat.)
Prince: What a beautiful stone castle!
(He goes in and finds the cook and her lazy helper sleeping in the kitchen. He finds the king and queen sleeping in the gold room.)

Prince: Are they all dead? No, they lie sleeping. I shall not disturb them.

(In the tower he sees the beautiful princess, who lies sleeping on the bed.)

Prince: Oh! Oh! The Sleeping Beauty!

(The prince touches her hand with his lips. The princess opens her eyes. The king awakes. So does the queen. The cook awakes. So does the kitchen boy.)

Cook: You lazy boy! You have been sleeping.

(The prince and princess go into the gold room. The king and queen welcome them. The twelve good fairies dance in a ring on the stone wall around the castle.)

The Fairies sing:

Disappear, you roses high.

Disappear into the sky.

The Sleeping Beauty woke today.

The hundred years have passed away.

What Do You Think? Locating speakers (play format)

Who said the princess would be sweet as a rose?
Who heard a noise on the tower stairs?

The River

Up in the mountains
Under the snow,
Close to the place
Where the snow flowers grow,
The river begins—and the cold drops slip
Over the stones with a drip, drip, drip.

More little drips,
More little drops
Run from the snow
On the mountain tops,
Meet with the others, more and more,
Until the stream tears down
  with a roar, roar, roar.

Down through the hills
Bright with rain
The stream speeds on
To the quiet plain
Where farms and houses and cities lie
And the wide stream slows to a sigh, sigh, sigh.

Wider and wider
The river grows
As on to the great
Gray sea it flows,
Until it empties in where sea gulls fish,
And turns into waves
   that go swish, swish, swish.

What Do You Think?   Sentence analysis (adverbial phrases)

Where does the river begin?
Where do the cold drops slip?
Where do the drips and drops run?
Where does the stream speed on?
Where does the river flow?

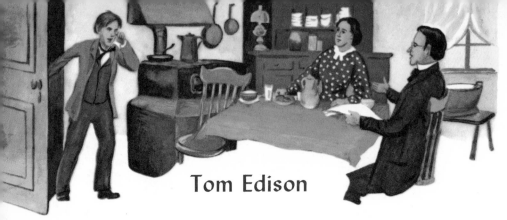

Tom Edison

"Tom! Breakfast is ready," called Mrs. Edison, putting the milk on the table.

"Yes, Mother, I'm coming!" answered Tom.

A few minutes later young Tom Edison walked into the kitchen. His boots were dusty, and his necktie was not straight. He was only half awake.

"What a sight you are!" said Mrs. Edison.

Mr. Edison put down his newspaper. "Tom," he said, "it is plain to see you're sleepy. At nine-thirty last night I asked you to go to bed. How late did you stay up?"

"I don't know, Father," answered Tom, "but I had to stay up. The boy next door was sending me signals on our telegraph. His signal came through to me very clearly. Our telegraph works."

"I don't care how many signals came through," Mr. Edison said. "Your experiments must stop. This last experiment of yours is the worst one so far. I want you to take down every inch of my wire. Imagine stringing it from tree to tree in our back yard!"

"I can't take the wire down," Tom insisted. "It's our telegraph wire."

"And my wire to begin with," repeated Mr. Edison plainly as he returned to his paper.

Mrs. Edison said, "Don't be too cross with Tom. Let him eat his breakfast. He mustn't be late for work. Remember, he's beginning his first job today. Not every boy of twelve can get a job selling newspapers on a train."

Tom was happy about his job on the train, which ran from his home town to a big city.

Every morning he got up at daybreak. He walked happily to the station and picked up a bundle of newspapers. After he had put them in the baggage car, he bought candy, fruits, and nuts. His job was selling all these things on the train.

Tom's job was hard, but he made good at it. When he arrived home at night, he always gave his mother some of the money he had earned during the day.

Tom's head was full of ideas. One day in the city he saw a load of vegetables. These vegetables were better than those at home, so he bought the load. He was able to sell them all in the station at home.

This gave Tom another idea. If everyone liked the vegetables, why not sell them from a stand in the station? He found a stand and got two friends to work for him. The vegetable stand brought Tom a lot of money.

With his money Tom bought chemicals and books. In his free time on the train he fixed up a small workshop in the baggage car. There he could study and experiment with his chemicals.

One day Tom saw a used printing press in a secondhand store.

"I should buy this old hand press," he thought to himself. "Then I could print a newspaper of my own. I could print hundreds of papers and sell them on the train."

Tom bought the printing press.

Then he asked the train conductor, "May I put the printing press in my workshop in the baggage car?"

The conductor threw back his head and laughed loudly. He thought to himself, "This boy has been to school only a few weeks in all his life. Then he didn't study much. I don't believe that he can even write. I wonder what he will do with a printing press."

But at last the conductor said, "It sounds like a silly idea to me, but go ahead. Put your printing press in the baggage car."

Tom Edison went ahead and printed the first copy of his newspaper, the first paper ever printed on a train. Soon the copies were selling like wildfire. So many passengers bought them that Tom printed seven hundred copies at a time.

Then one day a traveler from across the seas bought a copy. He liked it so much that he ordered a thousand copies.

Even the conductor began to feel proud of young Tom Edison. The paper had not been such a silly idea. As a matter of fact, it was making the train famous.

One day Tom was experimenting with his chemicals in the baggage car. Suddenly the train hit a cow on the tracks, and Tom's chemicals were knocked over. They dripped from the table and spread over the floor.

A fire started and began to spread quickly. In a flash, the floor of the baggage car was in flames. Tom threw water on the fire, but the flames kept spreading.

Tom cried out for help. The conductor came running and soon put out the flames. Then he looked at Tom.

"You have done all the harm you're going to do on my train," said the conductor angrily. "At the next station you and your chemicals and printing press must get off."

When the train reached the next station, the conductor ordered, "Get off!"

Tom could not believe his ears. He was so surprised he did not move.

Then the conductor pushed Tom out of the car and threw his belongings after him.

Tom walked sadly home. When Mr. Edison heard what had happened, he exclaimed, "Tom, you must give up these experiments!"

But Mrs. Edison said, "If Tom doesn't use any chemicals that start a fire, may he experiment in the attic?"

"All right," Mr. Edison said, "but if anything blows up, Tom will be sorry."

Nothing did blow up.

Tom Edison experimented during the rest of his eventful life. He invented more than a thousand things and became famous the world over.

Tom Edison invented parts for the electric telegraph. He invented the talking machine, the moving picture machine, and many electric things. One of the most important things he gave the world was the electric light.

What Do You Think?　　　　　　Context clues (opposites)

Tom's train job had a good <u>beginning</u> but a bad ____ .
Tom worked hard from <u>morning</u> to ____ .
He bought an <u>old</u> printing press, not a ____ one.
<u>Few</u> men have invented as ____ useful things as Edison.

152

Billy Whitemoon

Billy Whitemoon was a Winnebago Indian boy. He lived with his father and mother in a cabin near the Black River.

Billy liked to take part in the work of his tribe. One of the things he liked most was cranberry picking in the fall.

All the men and women and children of the tribe went to the cranberry swamp near the Winnebago lands. They would spend days picking the ripe cranberries, which they put in boxes and sent to the city.

Billy liked the winter, too. It was fun to go to school. When he wasn't in school, he skated with his friends on the river ice.

But when the heavy snow was gone from the Winnebago lands, Billy was very happy. He knew that spring had come.

One spring day Billy was walking through the woods. He heard a little moaning cry. There in the dry, dead leaves he saw a little fawn.

Billy went closer. He was surprised that the little fawn didn't run away. Billy knew that fawns were always very shy. Then he noticed that this one's leg was broken!

"Poor little fawn!" said Billy. "You just wait here. I'll be back soon."

Billy hurried to his cabin. Soon he returned with two straight sticks and some string. He tied the sticks to the broken leg. Then he picked up the fawn and carried it home.

When his father saw the fawn, he said, "What a beauty! He will make a good pet."

Billy loved all wild animals, but he loved the shy little fawn best of all. When the broken leg was better, Billy took the sticks off. Then he and the fawn would race together through the forest. Billy named his pet Lightfoot because he could run so fast.

Every spring Billy helped his father cut down young trees, which his mother used in making baskets.

Mother Whitemoon made baskets the way all Winnebago women did. She pounded the young trees into long strings. From the strings she made beautiful baskets.

Some of the baskets she colored red or blue or orange. She made her own paints from the roots that Billy gathered from the swamps. She had taught him to know the kind of roots used by Winnebago Indians for many, many years.

This spring Billy was delighted that the roots had made such beautiful colors. He knew that the baskets would sell well at their summer camp.

When warm weather came, the Whitemoons moved to their summer camp. They packed their kettles, blankets, clothes, and other baggage into their old car. They packed Mother Whitemoon's baskets carefully. Then they pushed Lightfoot into the car.

When everything was loaded, they started down the highway. They drove until they found a good place to camp for the summer.

Then Billy and his father built a summer house. They covered it with deer hides to keep the family dry in rainy weather. When their house was done, they built one for Lightfoot, too.

Every day Mother Whitemoon would put on a bright cotton dress and pretty earrings. Then she would sit in front of the summer house and sell her baskets. She let travelers who bought them take her picture.

When summer ended, the Whitemoons packed their belongings again. Then they crowded into the car with Lightfoot, who was much bigger now.

On their way back to their winter home, they stopped for a week to take part in the Winnebago Dance Time. At this season of the year all the Winnebago Indians camped near the river. They built campfires and danced every day.

Billy feasted on roast corn and baked fish. He listened to the stories and the songs of their tribe.

Billy wished he could sing some of the songs he was always making up. But he was too shy to sing in front of people. Only Lightfoot, his pet fawn, knew the songs that Billy could sing.

157

After the Dance Time was over, all the tribe returned to their winter cabins. Now it was the season for deer hunting. White men from the cities came to hunt in the forests near the Winnebago land.

Billy was glad that there was a law saying that no white man could hunt on Winnebago land. Lightfoot was so much bigger now that the hunters would surely shoot him.

One afternoon Billy was walking through the forest on his way home from school. He heard a rustle in the leaves. A short way ahead of him he saw Lightfoot coming to meet him!

The sight of his pet frightened Billy, for Lightfoot was off Winnebago land! If a hunter should see him, he would have the right to shoot. Billy looked around quickly to see if there was any danger. He heard the rustling of leaves!

His eyes caught sight of a red jacket. There was a hunter looking at Lightfoot. The man lifted his gun to his shoulder.

Billy shook with fear. Then in a flash he stepped between the hunter and Lightfoot.

"Get out of the way, boy!" shouted the hunter angrily. "You might get hit!"

"Oh, please!" Billy cried. "Don't shoot that deer! He's mine! He's mine!"

"How do I know he is your deer?" the hunter asked. "All deer look alike."

"Oh, but he is mine!" Billy insisted.

"You can't prove it!" the hunter said. He was still angry.

Billy knew how he could prove Lightfoot was his. If he sang, Lightfoot would come to him. No one had ever heard Billy's songs. The man might laugh at him, but he had to save Lightfoot.

Billy smiled shyly. Then he began to sing. "Come, Lightfoot, come here, come here. Come to me, my little deer!"

There was a rustling sound. Lightfoot came leaping through the woods toward Billy. He put his soft nose on his master's shoulder.

"You win!" said the hunter. "You have proved the deer does belong to you. I liked your song, too. You sing very well."

Billy was so pleased by the hunter's words that he told his mother and father what had happened. Then he sang for them, too.

Next year when the Winnebago Dance Time came, Billy sang for all the tribe. He was no longer shy as he sang his songs about the big world and the blue sky. He sang of the stars and the moon, and the brook that flows over the stones in the forest. He sang of the seasons of the year, and of Lightfoot, his wonderful pet deer.

He sang so well that the tribe called him "Billy Whitemoon, Maker of Beautiful Songs."

What Is the Meaning?
Billy was able to <u>prove</u> the deer was his.
to belong   to insist   to show by facts
He sang his songs because he was no longer <u>shy</u>.
angry   lazy   fearful

Study Pages

Last Sounds in Accented Syllables

First, look at the consonant letters at the left. Then say the key word and listen to the sound of those letters. Second, see what sound the letters have and listen for that sound in the words at the right.

LETTERS	KEY WORDS	SOUNDS	OTHER WORDS
d	fed	**d**	greedy, Edison
g(e)	cage	**j**	vegetable, stages
m	hum	**m**	chemical, famous
s	lies	**z**	season, thousand
t	sweet	**t**	beauty, forgot
gg	egg	**g**	baggage, digging
ck	pack	**k**	cricket, nickel
ch	such	**ch**	touching, peaches
dg(e)	edge	**j**	judging, bridges
ft	gift	**ft**	drifting, lifting
ld	wild	**ld**	shoulder, wildly
nd	pound	**nd**	spending, sandy

Which word means a kind of fruit?
Which word means a kind of insect?

Unaccented First Syllables

You know that many words have <u>accented</u> first syllables, as **greedy** and **cotton**.

A few words, however, have <u>unaccented</u> first syllables, as in **about** and **began.** You will find more words with different kinds of unaccented first syllables below.

FIRST SYLLABLE	KEY WORD	OTHER WORDS
a	about	awake, arrive
be	began	begin, behind
de	decide	delighted
ex	exclaim	experiment, explain
in	insist	inquire, invent
re	receive	repair, repeat

When you see one of the above syllables at the beginning of a word, you know it is unaccented. Then you will know the sound, too.

Hunt for a word above that means:
to do something again
to be very, very pleased
to ask a question
to fix something that is broken

Interesting Sayings

Goats are <u>light on their feet</u>.

The underlined idea above is one you may often see or use. Does it mean that there are electric lights on the feet of a goat? That would be a silly meaning. To be light on one's feet means to be able to pick them up so as to jump quickly or run fast.

Study the underlined parts of the sentences below. Decide upon the meaning of each part.

Susan <u>lost all track of time</u> when she got interested in reading a good book.

"I'll <u>give you a lift</u>," the kindly driver of the truck said to Jack.

The man liked the fawn so much that he said to Bob, "I'll buy that fawn <u>on the spot</u>."

It wasn't ten minutes before a motorboat came by to <u>pick up</u> the two boys on the island.

"Please <u>keep an eye on</u> my boys," Mrs. Packer said to the conductor of the train.

"Even a king must <u>keep his word</u>," stated the poor old fisherman.

Using What You Know

UNACCENTED SYLLABLE	CONSONANTS IN ACCENTED SYLLABLE	NEW WORDS
a of about	pr in press	
	ch in each	approach
a of about	gr in grease	agree
be of begin	s and d(e) in side	beside
de of delight	p in pop	
	nd in spend	depend
de of delight	scr in scratch	
	b(e) in tribe	describe
ex of explain	pr and ss in press	express
re of repair	m in mine	
	n in plan	remain

When you think the way another thinks, you _____ with him.

When you walk toward a fawn and get near the animal, you _____ him.

When you stand next to a goat, you are _____ him.

When you stay in one spot for two hours, you _____ there.

When you give facts about an insect that tell how it looks, you _____ it.

Rolling Plains

Dick Follows His Nose

At first Dick Campbell did not follow his nose. He followed his father and mother when they bought their tickets and boarded the river boat. He was traveling west to a new farm on the great prairie.

They had not been traveling long when Dick smelled food cooking. His nose guided him to where the smell came from. From deck to deck he went until he found the cook. He made friends with him at once.

The cook was a fat, jolly man. It was good to be one of the cook's friends. He made wonderful cakes with frosting half an inch thick. Sometimes he gave his friends two pieces of cake for supper.

Dick made friends with the pilot, too. Above the decks, Mr. Burnside stood at the big steering wheel and guided the boat down the long, muddy river.

As Mr. Burnside steered the boat, he told Dick many tales which described life on the muddy river.

"We used to live in Peachland," Dick explained, "but now we're moving west to a new farm on the prairie. Will this boat reach Prairie City by Friday?"

"Why do you have to be there by then?" inquired Mr. Burnside.

"Uncle George will meet us Friday in Prairie City," replied Dick. "He is going to drive us and all our baggage across the plains to our new farm."

Mr. Burnside looked at the sky.

"If the weather stays clear, we'll reach Prairie City by Friday," he said. "If we run into any fog, there's no telling when we shall arrive."

Mr. Burnside went on to describe the weather on the river.

"One minute it's sunny. Then a fog blows up," he said. "I can steer this boat through anything but fog. If we run into fog, we'll lose time. Everything depends on the weather."

During the trip up the river, there were many clouds in the sky. Sometimes there was rain, but so far there had been no fog.

On Friday morning, Dick followed his nose after a good smell. He had a cozy visit with the cook about something that was being baked for lunch.

Suddenly Dick saw that a cloud of fog was rolling up the river. He raced at once to the pilot house. "Mr. Burnside," he shouted, "the fog has come. Will we have to stop? Will we get to Prairie City today?"

"That depends," replied the pilot. "It depends on how thick the fog gets. If it gets much thicker, we'll lose time and have to stop. We don't want to wreck our boat."

Dick and Mr. Burnside watched the fog drifting closer and closer.

"Is it much farther to Prairie City?" inquired Dick in a disturbed voice.

"It's not far," replied the pilot, "but the fog is getting thicker, and we are losing time."

Dick tried to see ahead, but the boat was lost in a heavy fog.

"We'll have to stop," said the pilot. "Too bad, because we could reach Prairie City very soon if I could see to steer."

The steamboat stopped. All Dick could hear was the sound of the water swishing against the boat.

165

Dick looked at the fog. Suddenly he held his nose up. A smell was drifting through the fog. Dick sniffed. It was a smell he knew. He sniffed again.

"I smell apple pie," he said.

"That's good," said the pilot. "I'm glad the cook is fixing a real feast for lunch."

But Dick said, "Our cook isn't making apple pie for lunch. I saw him a few minutes ago. He was mixing a cake!"

"Then where would an apple-pie smell come from?" the pilot wanted to know.

Dick sniffed again. He held up one arm and pointed to the west.

"Out there somewhere," he answered.

The pilot tried to smell and said, "I have a cold in my head. I can't smell anything."

"I'm a good sniffer, and this is the best apple pie I ever sniffed," said Dick. "It can't be anything else."

The pilot was excited. "The smell must come from a house in Prairie City," he cried. "Describe it for me."

"It's a smell of sweet apples mixed with sugar," Dick said. "There's butter mixed with the sugar. Yes, lots of butter and sugar."

"Sweet apples, butter, sugar," sighed the pilot. "Those smells come from Aunt Jenny's house. There's no one else in Prairie City who can make such good apple pie. In fact, Aunt Jenny makes the best pie in the world."

"Does she bake it on Friday?" asked Dick.

"Yes," said the pilot. "Her house is near the wharf where we land. We could be there in no time if I could follow that smell."

"I'll be your guide," cried Dick. "Depend on me, my nose will tell us the way to Aunt Jenny's house." Dick sniffed the air.

"Steer to the right," he ordered.

The pilot steered to the right.

Dick sniffed again. "Now steer to the left," he said.

The pilot steered a little to the left. He followed all Dick's directions, while Dick followed his nose. It was a nose that could be depended on. It guided the pilot straight to the wharf at Prairie City.

"It's Friday!" laughed Dick as they jumped onto the wharf. "We reached Prairie City just as we planned."

"Yes," said the pilot. "And we made it just in time to have a piece of Aunt Jenny's wonderful apple pie! Come with me."

Aunt Jenny was so amused when she heard the story she laughed until the tears ran down her face. "Dick," she said, "no one else could have done it. You have earned all the apple pie you can eat!"

What Do You Think?   Drawing conclusions (related facts)

Around what time would this story be likely to take place? 1750 1850 1950

Johnny Big-Pockets

Johnny Parker lived on a farm in the Middle West with his father, his mother, his dog, and the hired man, Freddie.

Johnny always found many interesting things to do. He fed the chickens every day. He worked in the fields, too, helping to dig up the rich earth before the crops were planted.

Often Johnny would spend his time just looking for things. He found many treasures everywhere he went—in the earth and on top of the ground. Johnny thought most of the things he found were worth keeping. His pockets held them all.

This morning Johnny had found a stone. Perhaps it was an Indian arrowhead! He put it into the pocket of his blue jeans. Later, he found an old whistle he had once lost and forgotten about. He put it in his pocket.

After that, Johnny walked along a road that took him to the Greens' farmhouse. He knocked at the back door.

"Hello, Johnny," said Mrs. Green, who was sitting at the kitchen table. "I'm mailing a gift to my sister. I have some paper, but not a piece of string in this house! And I've forgotten to buy some every time I went to the store."

"Just a minute!" said Johnny. He began to dig into his pocket. Out came the whistle. There was the arrowhead. There was a dead insect in a little box. And there was a long piece of string, besides!

"You have saved my life!" Mrs. Green said with a smile. "I can mail this present when I go to town. Now what can I give you?"

Johnny looked around. On the table he saw a piece of sugar that had dropped from the sugar bowl.

"May I have that?" Johnny asked.

"Why, yes," said Mrs. Green. "And take another from the bowl to eat later."

Johnny ate one piece of sugar and put the other one in his pocket.

When Johnny got home, he stopped to visit with Freddie, the hired man. Perhaps Freddie had a new joke to tell.

Freddie was sitting in a chair, making out a list on a piece of paper. "Tomorrow is Saturday. That's going-to-town day," he said. "I'm making a list of the shopping I have to do. Oh, my! There goes my pencil point!"

"Just a minute!" exclaimed Johnny.

171

Out came the arrowhead, the dead insect, the whistle, and some leftover string. And there was a little chewed-up pencil, besides!

"How's this?" Johnny asked.

"Just wonderful," Freddie said.

That night before Johnny went to bed, he emptied the pockets of his blue jeans.

"Johnny, why on earth do you put everything into your pockets?" his mother asked.

"Because I need all these things," he said.

His mother shook her head. "These jeans are starting to wear out," she said. "I'll buy you some new ones in town tomorrow."

The next morning Johnny rode toward town with his father, mother, and the hired man. Suddenly Mr. Parker slowed the car.

"What's that up ahead?" he asked.

"That's Tom Bowling with his wagon and mules," Freddie said.

The wagon and mule team had stopped right in the middle of the road!

Everybody got out of the car.

"My silly mules won't move," Tom said.

Freddie tried pushing and Mr. Parker tried pulling, but the mules would not move from the middle of the road.

Johnny stood in front of the mules. He put his hands in his pockets. He hunted around until he found the sugar which he had put in his pocket the day before.

"Here, boys. Come get this, boys," he said. He held the sugar under each mule's nose and then backed away. The mules started to walk toward the sugar.

"They're moving!" Tom cried with delight.

The mules kept walking to town, and Johnny and his family rode on.

As soon as they were in town, Johnny's mother bought him new jeans. "You may wear them home," she said. "But I don't want you to put a thing in these pockets!"

Johnny walked out of the store beside his mother. He wondered what good jeans were if you couldn't put things in the pockets!

"Hello, Johnny!" said Mrs. Green on the porch of the store. "I just mailed the gift. I'm writing my sister. I'll tell her how you helped by giving me that string."

"Hello, Johnny!" said Freddie. He was carrying bundles and crossing off his list. "I'm still using your pencil!"

Tom Bowling called to Johnny, "Here's a piece of sugar for you. I just bought some for my mules. They won't stop on the road now!"

Johnny started to put the sugar in his pocket. But then he put it in his mouth.

When Johnny went to bed that night, he didn't have to empty a thing out of his pockets. But when he got up the next morning, he couldn't find his new jeans!

"Are you looking for these?" his mother said as she came into the room with the jeans.

Johnny put on the jeans. He put his hand in his pocket, and then his eyes grew wide.

His hand went far, far down before it reached the end of his pocket. He put his hand into the other pocket. It was just as big!

"How did I get such big pockets?" Johnny asked.

"I made them for you last night," his mother said. "Now eat your breakfast, Johnny, and then fill up your new pockets!"

What Do You Think? Context clues (homonyms)

When Johnny <u>rode</u> to town, he saw that the mules had stopped in the middle of the <u>road</u>.

When he _____ back home, he had on his new jeans.

His new pockets were big enough <u>to</u> hold arrowheads and many other things, <u>too</u>.

His mother had been very kind _____ him.

The Forgot Store

Mr. Cutter and his wife lived in a pretty, vine-covered house. The house stood at the crossing of two country roads. It was at the half-way point to town.

People coming down both roads used to stop at Mr. Cutter's house. One person would say, "Oh, Mr. Cutter, I forgot to buy some sugar when I went to town. Perhaps you could let me have a little. I need bread, too."

Another person would say, "Oh, I forgot to buy butter. Could you lend me half a pound? Will you lend me some jelly, too?"

After a time Mr. Cutter grew tired of lending things. He decided to build a store on his front porch and call it The Forgot Store. He planned to sell only things that people forgot.

176

On one shelf Mr. Cutter kept sugar. On another shelf he kept jelly. Other shelves held eggs, flour, milk, and things that women needed for their baking.

Every traveling man who came along tried to sell Mr. Cutter a case of something. Mr. Cutter could never say "No." Every day some new packing case would arrive.

One day a case of garden shovels arrived.

"How could anyone forget a shovel?" exclaimed Mrs. Cutter. "If a person needs something as big as that, he has it on his mind. He won't forget it."

But Mr. Cutter kept adding more things.

Now Mr. Cutter sold canned foods, such as creamed chicken, meat, and baked beans. He even sold yard goods of cotton and wool.

One day a little girl bought some jelly beans in town. On the way home she remembered that she had promised to buy some pencils for her brother. She went to the Forgot Store.

"I have paper," Mr. Cutter said, "but no pencils." After that he added pencils to his shelves.

One day a man named Bill Jones came into the store. He wanted a hunting knife. "I don't feel like going into town for it," he said.

Mr. Cutter said, "No, Mr. Jones, I won't sell you the knife. You didn't forget it. You're just too lazy to go into town. I sell only things people forget."

The more things people forgot, the more Mr. Cutter kept adding. Kettles! Wool gloves! Aprons! Ribbons! Straw hats! Birdseed! Woolen blankets! Rose bushes!

The front porch became so filled with things that Mr. Cutter needed the living room, too. He pushed the tables, chairs, and bookcases into the dining room.

Then he added dresses and hats.

"No woman would ever forget to buy a new dress or hat!" Mrs. Cutter exclaimed. "I want my living room back!"

But Mr. Cutter kept the living room and went on adding things to the shelves.

There were three special things in Mr. Cutter's store that he would not sell. Mr. Cutter liked those special things so much he kept them locked in a glass showcase. He hoped they would never be sold.

One of the things Mr. Cutter kept locked in the glass showcase was a jar of stick candy. It was such beautiful candy! Each piece was a foot long with colored stripes of yellow, rose, green, and light blue.

Beside the candy jar stood a small silver box. On a piece of white cotton in the box lay a string of beautiful beads. Each bead was a deep cranberry red.

One day a woman came in just as Mr. Cutter was dusting the beads.

"Oh, what beautiful beads!" she said. "I want them!"

"You didn't forget them," Mr. Cutter said.

"No, I didn't," the woman answered. "But I'll give you twelve dollars for them."

"I'm sorry, but I can't sell them," Mr. Cutter said. "No one forgot them."

Mr. Cutter didn't want to sell his beautiful striped candy or the red beads in the silver box. He wanted to keep them forever!

Another special thing in Mr. Cutter's showcase was a yellow box. When the cover of the box was lifted, out jumped a funny clown dressed in red and green! On the end of his pointed cap was sewed a glittering golden bell.

The jack-in-the-box clown had a special trick when he popped out. He would bow to the left, and then he would bow to the right.

Mr. Cutter hoped no one would ever say he forgot a jack-in-the-box!

Late one afternoon, a small boy came into the store.

"Hello, Tommy Beebee," smiled Mr. Cutter. "What did you forget today? I haven't seen any of you Beebees for a long time. You must not have been forgetting things."

"Oh, we have forgotten everything," cried Tommy. "My mother has been sick all winter! She has forgotten how to laugh. We have forgotten how to have fun at our house. And I almost forgot today is Mother's birthday. I want to buy her a special gift."

"Well, look around," said Mr. Cutter.

"Thank you!" said Tommy. "I have just one dollar to spend."

Tommy looked at each counter until he came to the glass showcase. He saw the jar of tall candy with the lovely stripes. He saw the beautiful red beads in the silver box.

"My mother loves stick candy and pretty beads," Tommy said. "I would like to buy both of them for her."

For a minute Mr. Cutter was disturbed. Should he sell these beautiful things? Tommy didn't say he had forgotten striped candy or red beads. But he did say he had forgotten to buy a gift.

"You may have some candy and the beads," said Mr. Cutter.

When Tommy started to leave with the presents, Mr. Cutter called after him, "Tommy, you forgot something!" He held up the yellow box. "It goes with the beads and the candy. See!"

Up popped the jack-in-the-box, bowing left and right. How Tommy laughed! How his eyes shone as he carried his treasures home!

And Mr. Cutter never forgot the happy look he helped put on Tommy's face.

What Do You Think?　　　　Drawing conclusions (related facts)

What do the facts prove:
about the place where Mr. Cutter had his store?
about the changes Mr. Cutter made in the store?
about the kind of man Mr. Cutter was?

A Letter from Grandfather

Green Valley Farm
Friday afternoon

Dear Children,

It was wonderful to get your letter last week. I would have answered sooner, but I've been cutting wheat this week. As you know, this is a busy time of year on the farm.

So you have been watching some interesting television shows! The one about the ship that made a trip to the moon must have been exciting. Perhaps when you are big, there will be such ships to take you from the earth to the moon.

184

Grandmother and I hope you won't forget what a wonderful world we have right here on earth.

As I write, it is a beautiful autumn day. Grandmother and I can always tell what season of the year it is by looking outside our kitchen window.

By looking for the right signs in our yard, we can always tell what season is approaching. Did you know that all plants and animals show signs of the different seasons?

Here in the North the days grow cool in autumn. Then the frost comes, and the leaves of the trees begin to lose their green color. As the days grow cooler and cooler, the leaves turn yellow, orange, and flaming red. Then they come rustling down to the ground.

When your father was a boy here on the farm, he always went hunting for nuts in the autumn. Butternuts and other nuts that are ripe drop to the ground. Squirrels gather the nuts then and hide them for winter food.

When winter approaches, things begin to freeze. Then many birds wing their way to the warm South. Some animals, like the woodchuck, crawl underground to sleep during the winter months.

Most animals that stay above the ground grow thicker fur. This keeps them from freezing. Not only do wild animals put on these heavy fur coats, but so do our cats and dogs.

Grandmother says that's why she has a fur coat to wear in the freezing weather, too!

Even the insects show signs of the different seasons. Grasshoppers and crickets hide their eggs in the earth before it gets cold.

Then, after autumn, winter really sets in, with its ice and snow.

In the winter months the earth freezes and becomes as hard as a rock. The plants that are left standing look dead. Only a few birds, such as snow birds, are seen.

Then comes spring! The earth awakes. The woodchucks, having slept long enough, come out. The eggs buried by the crickets and the grasshoppers become baby crickets and baby grasshoppers. Butterflies are seen again.

Many animals are born in the spring months. It's a pretty sight to see the shy newborn animals leaping in the fields.

New plants are set out in gardens, and growing things spring up from old roots. All the earth seems to be born again.

And then the summer months arrive. The wheat becomes ripe in the fields, and other crops are gathered. The vines grow thick, and the bees make honey in their hives.

Every season is interesting on the farm.

Has your father ever told you about the game we used to play? We called it "Name the Season." Each player has to make a list.

One list would say baseball, boat racing, football, and ice-skating. Other players would have to name the season for each game.

Another list would be of holidays. We would name the season for May Day, Fourth of July, Halloween, and New Year's.

We would make lists of farm crops. There's a season for nuts, corn, apples, wheat, hay, and peaches.

Grandmother and I play a new game when we get a letter saying you are coming to visit us. We start listing all the things we will do when you arrive. Next summer seems a long way off, but even now we are planning for your holiday with us.

Be sure to write us soon, and tell your father and mother "hello."

Love,
Grandfather

A Tree for Christmas

"Christmas just won't seem like Christmas without a tree," said Rosemary, looking up from her sewing. She watched her mother light a candle in the one-room prairie home.

The walls were made of blocks of earth, because there were no trees on the plains where the Fullers had settled. There had been no trees for building a cabin, no trees for making a wooden floor. And tomorrow there would be no tree for Christmas.

The door opened, and Rosemary's brother Paul came in, his head covered with snow.

"Ma," said Paul. "It's starting to storm outside. There's enough wind to blow the house down, and the snow is as fine as flour! Pa says it looks like a blizzard."

"A blizzard!" cried Ma. She ran to the door and threw it open. Rosemary was right behind her. Snow beat against their faces, and they could hardly see.

Pa was pushing his way to the door, leading two mules.

"Chester Fuller!" exclaimed Ma. "Where are you going with those mules?"

"Into the house, that's where!" said Pa. "The animals will freeze in the barn. We'll have to keep them in the house with us!"

Ma was so surprised that her mouth dropped open. Then she turned to Rosemary. "You and I will have to move things around to make room for the animals," she said.

As Rosemary listened to the storm beating against the house, she felt scared. Stories about prairie blizzards flashed through her mind.

But the scared feeling disappeared in a moment. The two mules looked so funny standing in the room that Rosemary and Paul started to laugh.

Pa tied the mules near the door. Then he and Paul went out to the barn again.

Rosemary and her mother cleared one side of the room by moving the table and chairs. They took the beds down and set the bed boards against the wall. Finally, they pushed boxes and trunks together to make a fence.

Paul and Pa made three more trips for the remaining animals. Finally, there were two mules, six chickens, a pig, and a cow fenced in a corner of the room.

Pa looked around at the crowded room. Suddenly he laughed and said, "It's a good thing we ate one chicken. I don't think there's room for one more!"

"Even if we had a Christmas tree," Rosemary agreed, "there would be no place for it."

But there was no time to worry about being crowded. There were homemade decorations to be put up. The fire was low in the stove, and supper was waiting to be cooked.

Later, as they were hanging the decorations, they heard a loud beating at the door. Pa walked to the door quickly and threw it open. For a moment he just stood there without saying anything.

"We'll have to make room for one more, after all," he said to Ma. "There's an Indian boy out here. We can't let him remain outside in this blizzard."

Ma agreed at once and asked the boy to come in. He moved slowly, as if his feet hurt him badly, and he looked scared. He told the Fullers his name was Red Deer. He had been caught in the blizzard while hunting.

Everybody tried to make the Indian boy feel at home. Pa took one look at the boy's feet and said, "Frostbite!"

After Pa took care of the frostbite, Paul set up a bed for Red Deer. Then Ma gave him some hot food and dry clothes.

Sitting up in bed in the middle of the room, Red Deer watched with interest as the family put up the remaining decorations.

There were no evergreens, but the Fullers had made red and green candles. The other decorations were made of paper saved for many months.

Paul and Rosemary were hanging strings of popcorn and colored stars around the room. Red Deer watched them shyly without saying anything. Finally, he asked Paul what they were doing.

Paul explained to the Indian boy that tomorrow would be a special holiday that is called Christmas. The family would give gifts to one another and sing Christmas songs. "It is a happy holiday," he said.

"It should be happy," Rosemary agreed, "but it will not be very happy this year. We won't be able to have a tree."

"White girl like tree?" asked Red Deer.

Rosemary explained that where they had come from, there were many trees. "Every family has a tree in the house for this special holiday," she said. "But here on the prairie there are no trees for Christmas."

Quickly she began to draw a picture of a Christmas tree. She showed it to Red Deer.

"Tepee," he said, pointing to the picture.

Rosemary laughed. She agreed that the shape of her drawing did look something like the shape of a tepee. She thought a moment, then added a star and other decorations to her tree. "Not tepee," she said, showing the drawing to Red Deer again. "Christmas *tree*. Do you understand?"

The boy smiled. "Red Deer understand," he said. "White girl is sad. Without this, happy holiday is not happy."

Ma was listening as she spread blankets on the floor for the family to sleep on. "It will be a happy holiday," she said. "Just wait until tomorrow morning. You will see!"

Rosemary was the first to awake the next morning. The wind had stopped. The room was cold and still. "I hope we aren't snowed in," she thought, getting up to look outside.

As she started across the room, she saw something that made her forget all about the blizzard. "Oh, my!" she said in a loud voice.

Pa jumped up and reached for his gun. "What's wrong?" he cried.

"Look!" said Rosemary.

In a house overflowing with too many things, Red Deer had made room for one more.

The bed boards that had been against the wall were now on Red Deer's bed, standing in the shape of a tepee. His blanket was pulled around the boards, and it was covered with the Fullers' Christmas decorations.

Red Deer pointed proudly. "It's for your holiday," he said. "A *tree-pee* for Christmas."

The Moving House

Walking home one evening
We met a funny load—
A wooden house was being pulled
By horses up the road.

Through windows without curtains
We saw its papered walls,
Its stairs going up and coming down
Between two little halls.

And no stove in the kitchen.
And it was sad somehow.
We wished a voice would call, "Oo-hoo,"
Or "Supper's ready now."

197

Bill Cody, Winner of the West

In the early days of our country, the West was a wild place. Wild buffaloes lived on the plains and fed on the prairie grass. They were hunted for their meat which was fed to the men building the railroad to the West.

The most famous buffalo hunter of all time was Bill Cody. He brought in so many buffaloes that he earned the name Buffalo Bill.

Buffalo Bill had a good life on the plains. Each day was filled with everything he liked —danger, good horses, and a part in building the West.

He held many jobs during his long life. His first important job was carrying the mail with the Pony Express.

Bill Cody was only fifteen years old when he was hired by the Pony Express. Some men thought there was too much danger for a boy. But Bill Cody proved he was quick with a gun and a good rider.

The Pony Express covered nearly two thousand miles of wild trails. There were canyons where Indians would hide, waiting to shoot the riders and take their horses. Robbers, too, often hid at the passes and tried to hold up the mail.

The riders of the Pony Express carried a special mailbag made to hang over a very light saddle. This special saddlebag had a pocket in each of its four corners. Three pockets held the through mail, and the fourth carried mail for the stations along the trail.

"The Boys of the Pony," as the riders were called, made history. With great speed they changed horses and picked up mail at each station. In its day, the Pony Express was the fastest carrier of mail in the world.

One day the rider from the east was late in reaching Bill's station.

"I wonder if he has run into trouble," Bill said, patting Prince, his horse. He watched for a cloud of dust made by a horse's hoofs, the first sign of an approaching rider. At last he saw the dust and heard hoofbeats.

The rider galloped in with bad news. "Black Marlin, the outlaw, is hidden along the trail!" he said. "He is waiting to rob the Pony."

"That must mean we are carrying a lot of money on this trip, doesn't it?" asked Bill.

"Fifty thousand dollars!" answered the rider. "Wait until tomorrow. If the Pony doesn't go through today, Marlin will know we have been warned. He may move on."

"He may," said Bill, "but I was hired to carry the mail. I am riding today."

"What will you do if you meet Marlin?" asked the station keeper.

"I'll be ready for him," Bill replied. "He wants a saddlebag, and he will get one!"

Bill ran into the station and picked up an empty saddlebag. He explained his plan to the keeper and the rider as he filled the pockets with paper. Now the bag looked as if it were full of mail or money.

Bill picked up the saddlebag and hurried back to Prince, who stood waiting with the mailbag over the saddle. Bill took off the bag and saddled Prince again, hiding the bag full of money under the saddle blanket. Over the saddle he threw the bag full of paper.

"You are riding straight into trouble if you meet Marlin," insisted the keeper.

"I know that," Bill agreed, "but if my plan works, the mail goes through."

Bill jumped into the saddle and called, "Let's go, Prince. We're late." Then, bending low over Prince's neck, he galloped away.

Bill rode fast. He watched for signs of the outlaws. The plain was broken only by the sandy hills in the distance. There was no sound but the pounding of Prince's hoofbeats on the hard dry trail.

Bill was heading for a narrow canyon where the stony trail ran between two hills.

"If I can get through that canyon, I can make the first station," he thought.

As Prince approached a bend in the trail, two men stepped out, blocking the narrow stony pass. They held their guns ready to fire.

"Reach for the sky!" ordered one of the men.

"Get down and throw us your saddlebag," said the other outlaw, narrowing his eyes.

"If I seem too willing, they may guess there is something wrong," thought Bill.

So Bill said to the outlaws, "I will not throw the bag. It is carrying the mail."

"And fifty thousand dollars!" added one man.

"Are you Black Marlin?" asked Bill.

"I am," said the outlaw.

"Robbing United States mail will get you into trouble," said Bill, jumping to the ground.

"Let me worry about that," laughed Marlin.

"All right." Bill started to take the bag from the saddle. Then he turned quickly and threw it with all his might at Marlin's head.

The sudden move surprised the outlaws. As he stepped back, Marlin tripped over a rock and fell to the ground. The other outlaw was bending over to pick up the bag.

At that very moment Bill took out his gun. "Throw down your guns!" he ordered.

Still keeping them covered, Bill mounted. Then he galloped away fast toward the west.

Bending over Prince's neck, Bill spoke in his ear. "Come on, old boy!" he said. "I'm depending on you."

Bill looked back over his shoulder. The outlaws were opening the saddlebag. Suddenly one of them reached for his gun and fired. The bullet whistled over Bill's head. Again and again the outlaws fired, but the bullets all went wild.

In a few seconds Bill had put a great distance between himself and the outlaws.

Bill galloped into the next station on time. He told the station keeper about his adventure with Marlin and the other outlaw.

"Another wonderful ride by a Boy of the Pony!" the keeper said. "You're a hero!"

Bill Cody and the other Boys of the Pony had many exciting adventures. They rode the hard trails and carried the mail for only a year and a half. At the end of that time the Pony Express was no longer needed. Telegraph wires had reached from the East to the West.

After riding for the Pony, Bill went from one adventure to another. He became a driver of a stagecoach that traveled over the old Pony Express trail. In this job, too, he proved himself a hero. Later, he became a famous Indian fighter and buffalo hunter.

As time went on, railroads took the place of stagecoaches. Buffaloes disappeared from the plains, and the Indians and white men stopped fighting one another.

Bill Cody's last adventure was founding Buffalo Bill's Wild West Show. He brought together many of the old heroes of the West, Pony Express riders, hunters, guides, Indians, and Indian fighters.

The show traveled all over the country, telling the story of the building of the West.

What Do You Think? Sequence

In what order did these events take place?
Cody earned the name Buffalo Bill.
Bill Cody carried mail with the Pony Express.
Cody founded a famous Wild West Show.
Bill drove a stagecoach over an old trail.

The Mule-eared Squirrel

High up in the cottonwood tree sat Jack, the mule-eared squirrel. He was watching what was happening in the camp below.

This camp was in a canyon which had once been a favorite spot of the Indians. Now some workmen were using the camp. Inside their log cabin were low, narrow beds on which the men slept.

Jack was a little shy of the strangers, but his eyes shone with joy as he watched them from a distance.

After dark, Jack looked all around. He was glad that the firelight did not shine on the hollow in the tree where he lived.

He lay quietly in his cozy hole, listening to the strange noises below.

Before long, Jack heard a beautiful sound. The mule-eared squirrel did not know what music was. But the sound made him happy from the top of his furry head down to his tiny feet. He moved closer and listened with his big ears to the delightful sounds.

Joe Hall, the cook, was playing on his mouth organ. Jack was pleased with the sweet tunes that drifted through the air. His body trembled, and his head swam with joy. He wanted to dance and do other silly things.

Jack was a wild squirrel, but the music made him forget his fear.

One day when Jack went into the camp, Joe threw a sugar-coated cookie to him. Jack liked the sweet cookie. After that, he began to lose his wild ways. He went about the camp as freely as the workmen themselves.

Every night Jack listened to the music that Joe made with his mouth organ. Soon Jack became a great favorite with all the workmen in the camp.

Jack began to take away small things which he found lying near the log cabin. He thought the knives and tin plates looked pretty. He hid a few in his favorite spot.

One night Joe Hall left his mouth organ lying on a camp chair. Jack took the mouth organ and hid that, too.

Then there was no more music in camp. This made Jack very unhappy. Every evening he sat on a branch of his tree, waiting for Joe to play the mouth organ.

Jack did not know that the music came from the shiny stick with holes in its sides. He had hidden that stick in a pile of wood near the cabin. Jack stored most of his favorite treasures in that woodpile.

One day Polaski, the leader of the workmen, left an open box lying near the camp. The box was full of bullets. Jack's black eyes shone with joy when he saw them.

He carried the bullets away one by one to a hollow log in the woodpile.

A few evenings later, a strange man rode into camp, bringing with him a heavy leather bag tied to his saddle. He was welcomed with shouts of joy from all the men.

Jack sat on his branch and watched the strange man give each workman pieces of green paper. The mule-eared squirrel could not understand what made the men act so happy. Then the stranger took from the bag round pieces of something that was as shiny as tin. He threw them on the table.

Jack planned to carry away some of these bright and shiny things.

After the strange man left, the workmen put the green paper and shiny things away. Jack had never seen them be so careful.

The next day all the workmen went to the
other side of the canyon. Shortly after they
left, Jack saw two strangers creep out of the
bushes near the stream. Jack had seen bobcats
creep up on rabbits just like that.

Joe, the cook, was sitting with his back
against the cottonwood tree. The little
squirrel's heart beat fast. He wanted to let
his friend know that danger was near.

"Br-r-r-r!" Jack warned from his branch.
But he was unable to make Joe understand.

The strangers began to creep toward Joe.
Soon they were right behind him. The next
moment one of them hit the cook on the
head, knocking him over.

The other man tied Joe's hands and feet with a rope. No matter how hard he tried, the cook could not free himself.

Jack watched as the strangers searched the camp. He saw them take the green paper from its hiding place.

Then he saw the men carry tin cans of food out of the cabin. One of the men brought logs from the woodpile and built up the fire under the kettle.

"Bang! Bang!" The noise made Jack's heart go patter-patter. A burning stick hit one of the men, who thought it was a bullet.

The other man dropped the green paper and started to run. "Bang! Bang!" came the noise again. The next moment both men were running away.

Polaski and the workmen hurried up the trail. They cut the rope and freed Joe.

"Robbers wanted our money," said Joe.

"There's one thing I don't understand," said Polaski. "Who did the shooting?"

"Jack did," Joe replied. "You remember those bullets that disappeared? He must have hidden them in the woodpile. When the robbers built the fire, the bullets went off. Jack's the hero!"

"Jack's mischief saved our money," Polaski agreed.

The men searched the woodpile and found many things they had missed. During their search they found Joe's mouth organ where Jack, the mischief maker, had put it.

That night Joe played his mouth organ. On his branch, Jack tried to dance.

"Look at our mischief maker!" cried Polaski with a hearty laugh. "See him dance!"

At that moment Jack's life was full of joy once more.

Study Pages

Sounds and Consonant Letters

Say the first word and listen to the sound of the letter or letters in dark print. Then say each of the other words and listen for the same sound. Decide what letter or letters stand for the sound.

KEY WORD	OTHER WORDS
fog	telegraph, buffalo, enough
jar	jeans, jelly, baggage
shoo**k**	deck, case, chemical
hoo**ks**	mix, attics, sticks
ha**ng**	bang, song, wing
ba**nk**	think, blanket, trunk
set	sold, press, cent
shape	shelf, sugar, special
su**ch**	approach, adventure, mischief
thick	teeth, thousand, thirty
these	weather, themselves, gather
zoo	freeze, blizzard, music

Find a word that begins like **think** and means "ten times one hundred."

Vowel Sounds in Accented Syllables

Say each key word and its vowel sound. Then say the words at the right and decide in which syllable the same vowel sound is heard. Last of all, tell what letters stand for the sound.

KEY WORDS	OTHER WORDS
ate	awake, remain, mailing
get	adventure, forget, weather
eat	beating, agree, creeping
it	distance, blizzard, silver
side	guided, lying, describe
hot	holiday, forgot, pocket
go	Cody, approaching, flowing
cut	rustle, become, honey
use	music, beauty, fewer
hall	always, thoughtful, crawling
jar	market, harmful, tomorrow
her	person, searching, disturb

Find a word with the same vowel sound in the accented syllable as the word at the left. It must have the meaning given at the right.

rope	Coming near, drawing close to
star	The day after today
lend	An exciting event, trip, or happening

Ideas in Parts of Words: un

1. Jack dropped the glass, but it was unbroken.

The first syllable **un** tells you that the glass was not broken. It means "not."

2. Tom unloaded the truck.

The first syllable **un** tells you that the load was taken from the truck. It means "taken from."

3. Susan unlocked the door.

The first syllable tells you that Susan did the opposite of locking the door. This syllable **un** means "opposite."

Read each sentence. First find a word with the first syllable **un.** Then decide if the use of **un** is like **1, 2,** or **3,** above.

Frank thought the prize he won was unearned.

The family decided to unpack their baggage.

Polly unhooked her dog's chain.

The fox escaped from the fight unharmed

Steps to New Words

New word: **thunder**

1. In how many places do you see vowel letters?
   a. Is there a sounded vowel in each place?
   b. Then how many syllables does the word have?
2. Which syllable is likely to be accented?
   a. What rule helps you know the vowel sound in this syllable?
   b. Say the vowel sound in the accented syllable. Say the accented syllable.
3. What letters stand for the unaccented syllable? Say the word, using the sound of those letters as an unaccented syllable.
4. What does the word mean?

Another new word: **intend**

Use the above steps. You may want to do step **3** before finishing step **2,** however, because the unaccented syllable comes first.

Do the same with each new word below.

    fellow   descend   needle

Which new word means?

    to have in mind a plan

    to come down or go down from a higher place

Cowboy Trails

The Song That Cows Do Not Like

Bob Butterfield had been born in Maine and had lived there for all of his nine years. But a month ago his father had bought a large ranch. Now Bob had come to live in Texas on the Circle O Ranch.

One of his greatest joys was helping the hired hands. Bob was learning to rope cattle. He hoped to become a ranch hand himself.

Tonight he was very proud because his father was letting him ride with the cowboys. He had to prove that he was worthy of the new saddle and rope that his father bought yesterday.

Bob rode beside a cowboy named Texas Gus. They circled slowly around the sleeping cattle.

Texas Gus said, "Our job is to keep those cattle quiet. If they hear a noise they don't like, they wake up and run. They run for miles, and nothing can stop them."

Off in the distance a cowboy was singing, "Give me my boots and saddle."

"He's making a noise," said Bob. "Will that disturb the cattle and wake them?"

"No," said Texas Gus in a lazy voice. "Our singing agrees with the cattle. It's their favorite music. Cowboy songs are soft and slow. They put the cattle to sleep just as bedtime songs put babies to sleep."

Bob chuckled at the idea.

"Why are you chuckling?" asked Gus.

"Singing to cows," Bob chuckled again. "Men singing songs to big old cows."

"It sounds silly," Texas Gus agreed, "but you'll soon see that cows like our tunes."

Texas Gus and Bob rode quietly along an old buffalo trail that crossed wide plains bright with moonlight.

Finally the silence was broken by Texas Gus. He said, "There's one song I know that cows don't like."

"How do you know the cattle don't like it?" Bob asked.

"Well, I'll tell you," Texas Gus said. "It's a funny thing. It happened before your father hired me."

"Once I sang that song when I was working on another ranch," Texas Gus went on. "The cows acted as if they heard a wolf or a mountain lion. They jumped up, swished their tails, threw their heads up, and ran away. Some of those cows haven't been seen since."

Bob said, "Well, don't you sing that song tonight. You'll scare my father's cattle, and he will be sorry he hired you."

Texas Gus shook his head sadly. He said, "Sometimes a song runs through my mind until I just have to sing it. That has happened three times. The cows ran for all they were worth every time."

They rode on in silence. All Bob could hear was the beat of horses' hoofs.

Finally, Texas Gus started to speak. "It's a long time since I've wanted to sing that song," he said. "But the music is creeping into my mind right now."

Bob was worried. His father's herd of cattle might get scared if Texas Gus sang the song that cows do not like.

Bob watched carefully. Texas Gus opened his mouth to sing. "No!" begged Bob.

Texas Gus closed his mouth. He shook his head. He did not sing. But he said, "You'll have to let me sing that song tonight."

"Do me a favor," begged Bob. "Think about something else, maybe cattle rustlers."

They rode on, circling the sleeping herd. Texas Gus began to hum.

Some of the cows pawed the earth and swished their tails. A steer jumped up, threw back his head, and moaned.

"Stop!" begged Bob. "You'll wake up the cows! Sing *My Old Kentucky Home,* or anything else."

Texas Gus stopped. He scratched his head. "I'm an understanding man, but I just have to sing it sometime tonight," he insisted.

They rode on in silence. They did not speak, but each had his own thoughts.

"How do you keep a cowboy's mouth shut?" Bob wondered.

Suddenly an idea flashed into his head. He reached into his pocket and pulled out a paper bag. In it was a pound of mixed gumdrops. He watched Texas Gus carefully.

218

In a moment the cowboy's lips began to move. He started to hum in a slow, lazy way. Then he opened his mouth to sing.

Bob worked fast. He pulled out a sugary gumdrop. He leaned over and popped the gumdrop right into the cowboy's open mouth.

"Have a gumdrop," he said.

Texas Gus opened his eyes wide in surprise when he tasted the gumdrop. He shut his mouth and chewed. Each bite tasted better. He could not sing while he chewed.

When the gumdrop had disappeared, Bob took another one out of the bag. He waited and watched.

Soon the lips of the cowboy moved again. He began to hum. He opened his mouth. Bob popped another gumdrop into it. Again the trick worked. While he was busy chewing, Gus was unable to sing.

Bob had a pound of gumdrops. Every time Gus opened his mouth to sing, Bob leaned over and popped a gumdrop into Gus's mouth.

It took a long time for Texas Gus to eat all the gumdrops. They kept his mind off the song that cows do not like. When he had finished the gumdrops, the song was not running through his mind any more.

Bob was glad about that. Now his father's herd would not be scared.

But Bob was disturbed about one thing. All the gumdrops had disappeared. He had not tasted even one. But he felt like a hero, for he had kept the cowboy's mouth shut.

Just then Texas Gus began to speak. "I haven't had such tasty gumdrops since I was a boy. Now let me do a favor for you."

Texas Gus reached into his pocket. Then he leaned over and handed Bob a bag of jelly beans.

"Jelly beans!" chuckled Bob. "My favorite candy! I like them even better than gumdrops."

List the jobs of cowboys.
List the states Bob had lived in.

A Carol for the Mayor

It was a winter night in a little town in Texas. Glittering stars danced in the sky. Candlesticks with lighted candles stood in windows. It was the night before Christmas.

In a house in the middle of the town, Alice Spillman ran to answer the telephone. She talked for a while and then put the receiver down. "What bad luck!" she cried.

Mrs. Spillman came hurrying from the company-filled living room. When she saw Alice's tears, she shut the hall door and asked, "What's the matter, Alice?"

"That was Jean," said Alice through her tears. "She telephoned that the girls can't go. Tonight we were to sing Christmas carols for the people who live on this block."

When Grandfather Spillman heard Alice's voice, he left the aunts and uncles and cousins in the living room. The Spillmans had come from every part of the state of Texas to spend the holiday together.

In the hall Grandfather looked at Alice over his glasses. "Tears at Christmas?" he asked. "This is the time to be merry."

"Oh, Grandfather!" Alice cried. "A month ago four of us girls planned to sing carols on the night before Christmas. But now no one can go. All our plans are spoiled."

Grandfather held Alice's hand in his own. Suddenly he exclaimed, "I have an idea! Will you let me ask some people to take the place of your friends?"

"Where will you get them?" Alice asked.

Grandfather pointed toward the living room. "I'll ask every person in there to join us," he said. "Would you like that?"

Alice started to say "No." She felt shy about caroling with grown people.

Before Alice could speak, Grandfather went into the living room. Some of the aunts, uncles, and cousins were sitting there talking. They were catching up on all that had happened since they had seen each other last.

"How would you like to join Alice and me in a little fun tonight?" asked Grandfather.

Then he told the company about Alice's bad luck. "Her friends can't go," he said. "Will you go instead?"

"You mean you want us to go caroling?" a cousin inquired.

"That's what I mean," Grandfather stated. "But hurry. Alice must hang up her Christmas stocking and get to bed early."

Everyone got up at once, hurrying into hats and coats.

Out into the cool evening went all the Spillmans. Along the street, Christmas greens were hanging in every doorway. In the front yards grew little berry trees. Their branches were covered with white berries.

The Spillmans approached a house and stood in a circle in front of it.

"What shall we sing?" Grandfather asked.

"I like *We Three Kings,*" Alice answered. She had learned it at school and could play it on the organ. Now she hummed the tune, and the others joined in merrily.

After that, they walked slowly through the town, caroling as they went. Here and there, window shades went up and happy faces looked out at the carolers.

"I thought we were going only around the block," Alice said in a low voice. "Instead, we're walking all over town."

"Christmas is for everybody," Grandfather answered merrily. "We'll put a carol in the Christmas stocking of everyone in town."

So the Spillmans sang for people of all ages. They sang for newborn babies, young children, and old people. They sang at new houses that had silver knockers on their doors. And they sang at houses that were weathered with age.

Then they walked up Berry Hill. At the top, old Mrs. Case lived alone. There was a lot of room in her house now, for her sons had grown up and moved away. One of them was the mayor of a large Texas city.

"We're in luck," Grandfather said. "Mayor Case is home for the holidays. The newspaper said he needs a rest."

"But, Father," said Mrs. Spillman. "Mrs. Case always leaves her shades up. Tonight they are pulled down. That means the mayor doesn't want to be disturbed."

"You may be right," said Grandfather.

"The lights are still on," said Alice. "The mayor must be awake. Let's just sing one carol very softly. That won't disturb anyone."

Grandfather agreed. "I've discovered that there's nothing like a song to rest a body," he said. "What shall we sing, Alice?"

"Let's sing *Joy to the World,*" Alice said.

So the Spillmans sang the well-known carol. They sang more softly and more sweetly than ever before.

Suddenly a shade went up in the living room. Mayor Case stared out at the carolers for a moment. Then the door opened. In the doorway stood the mayor and his mother.

"Merry Christmas!" he called. "Thank you so much for that beautiful carol. You can't imagine how good it has made me feel."

"Merry Christmas to you, Mayor," said Grandfather. "We're glad you liked our song."

Then he pushed Alice to the front. "This little lady is the one you must thank for our caroling tonight," he said.

226

"Thank you, young lady," said the mayor as he shook Alice's hand. "We were feeling sad tonight until we heard your sweet carol. Won't you please come in?"

As the Spillmans entered the house, Mrs. Case offered them mixed candies and fruit.

Before they left, the mayor gave Alice a gift. "Here's something for your Christmas stocking," he said. "It was mine when I was your age." He handed her a silver music box.

Alice stared at the beautiful silver box. "For me!" she cried with delight.

"For you," said the mayor. "For bringing good cheer and for helping me discover how much good neighbors are worth."

The Spillmans went home, singing. Alice was proud of the grownups in her family and of the joy they had given their neighbors.

What Do You Think? Shifts of meaning

The girls hoped to sing carols to people on their <u>block</u>, but something happened to <u>block</u> that plan.
come in the way of   part of a city

A Day in Mexico

Polly was excited! She was on her way to Mexico at last! Although she lived in Texas, she had never visited Mexico. Today her Uncle Frank was driving her there, together with her cousins, Jane, Tom, and Peter.

At noon the car left Texas and entered Mexico. Ahead of them the children could see the little dusty village they would visit.

When they entered the village, Uncle Frank drove straight to the open-air market.

He gave each of the four children a quarter to spend. "Look around the market," he said, "and see who can buy the best souvenir."

"What is a souvenir?" asked Polly.

"Something to keep," Uncle Frank explained, "to help you remember Mexico."

So Polly, Jane, Tom, and Peter started for the market to spend their quarters.

A young bootblack without shoes or stockings ran up to Polly. "Shine, *amiga?*" he asked brightly. "The price is ten cents."

He carried an old box hanging on a rope around his shoulder. His merry eyes traveled to Polly's feet.

Polly shook her head. Her shoes were clean and shiny. The bootblack shut his box and turned sadly away.

Polly and her cousins joined the crowd that was entering the market. Everyone was speaking Spanish. Although the children could not understand a word of that language, they thought the people were friendly. Polly heard someone say the word *amiga.*

"I wonder what that word means," Polly thought. "The bootblack said *amiga,* too. I wish I knew this language."

229

On the stands in the market were many souvenirs from which to choose. There were straw baskets, straw horses, and big straw hats. Brightly colored blankets, silver beads, painted toys, and jackknives were sold, too.

The two boys walked in one direction, while Polly and Jane went in another.

Soon the girls reached a doll stand. All the dolls were dressed in perfect copies of the clothes that girls and ladies wear in Mexico.

Some of the dolls had on long black dresses and black netting over their heads and shoulders. Others were dressed in bright clothes with stripes of many shades. All the dolls had on long stockings.

There were so many dolls that Jane found it hard to choose one. While she was trying to decide, she said to Polly, "What are you going to buy with your quarter?"

"I can't decide," answered Polly. "I don't want a doll. I'll meet you later. I'm going to search the market for my souvenir."

As Polly walked through the market, she met Uncle Frank. He was looking at the striped wool blankets which some men in Mexico wear in place of coats.

Then she met her cousin Peter. One of the market women had just sold him a straw animal. Next, she met her cousin Tom, who was looking at a pig bank made of clay.

Farther on, Polly came to a stand where clay jars were sold. They were splashed with the brightest colors she had ever seen.

Polly thought, "I'll choose one of these clay jars. It will be a perfect souvenir of Mexico."

So she asked the lady the price of a jar.

"One quarter, *amiga*," replied the lady.

231

Just as Polly was opening her pocketbook to take out the quarter, she heard a baby cry. She turned and saw a brown-faced baby sitting on its mother's lap.

"What is the matter?" Polly asked.

"My baby wants oranges," replied the mother, looking at a fruit stand.

"Poor baby!" Polly thought. Although she wanted a jar, she bought two oranges for a nickel and gave them to the baby.

"Thank you, *amiga*," said the mother.

There again was that Spanish word *amiga*. Polly smiled at the mother and walked along the row of stands. Her quarter had turned into twenty cents. Now she could not buy the clay jar. What could she choose instead?

Suddenly a man called, "May I take your picture? I will take it on this donkey for twenty-five cents. I will lend you a blanket made in Mexico to put around your shoulders. You'll find a picture of you on a donkey will make a perfect souvenir."

Polly said, "I wish I could have my picture taken with something from Mexico. But I have only twenty cents."

"For twenty cents I will take it without the blanket," said the man.

Just then a little girl stepped up. "My name is Rita," she said shyly. "I am from Mexico. I will sit on the donkey behind you. I will put my arms around you—free."

So Polly and Rita had their picture taken together sitting on the donkey's back. When it was finished, Rita was eager to see it. She was so pleased with the picture that Polly said, "Keep it. It will be your souvenir."

Rita thanked Polly for the gift and ran off with the picture. Polly was still without a souvenir, and her quarter was gone.

Just then the man handed her two cents in change. "You do not have to pay twenty cents," he said. "Instead, I'll make a special price because you are Rita's *amiga*."

Now there remained only two pennies with which to buy a souvenir of Mexico. As Polly looked at the different stands, she heard a voice she knew. "Shine, *amiga!*" it said. "Two cents. It's a special price."

The little bootblack was smiling so eagerly that Polly just had to say "Yes."

The bootblack set down his old shoe box. Polly put her foot on the box. She watched his flashing brown hands shine her shoes.

"They look very pretty," said Polly as she handed him her last two pennies. "I don't understand the Spanish language. Will you please tell me what *amiga* means?"

"Amiga means friend, if your friend is a girl," the boy explained. "If your friend is a boy, he is called *amigo."*

Polly felt that the little bootblack was now her friend. She asked him his name.

"In your language it is Johnny," he said.

"Good-by, *amigo,"* she said to him.

"Good-by, *amiga,"* he said to her.

Just then Uncle Frank and Polly's cousins joined her. They were eager to show their souvenirs. Uncle Frank had a blanket. Peter had a straw donkey. Tom had a painted pig bank, and Jane carried a doll.

"What did you choose?" Jane asked.

"Two *amigas* and one *amigo!"* Polly said.

"What are they?" asked Tom.

"Friends!" Uncle Frank said. *"Amigos* in Spanish. That's a special kind of souvenir that can't be bought or sold."

"I've discovered that," said Polly, smiling happily. She would never forget Mexico, the home of her three *amigos.*

King of the Range

Tom Bowman looked with longing at the rope that belonged to his brother Jim. How Tom had begged for a rope! But his father said he must wait until he was older.

The cowboys were going out on the range the next day to search for wild horses. These horses made fine ranch horses once they were caught and tamed. Tom could go along with the cowboys, but just to watch.

At their camp that evening, Tom tried to rope a pony. He was using a rope which belonged to one of the other cowboys. He heard his brother chuckling.

"Oh, Baby," Jim called. "Come over here and watch a real roper."

Tom didn't like to be called "Baby."

Just then the ponies nearby grew restless. A sound like thunder came across the range.

"Is that thunder?" Tom asked.

"It's Proud Pirate," Jim replied. "I saw him the other day when I was riding fence for another rancher."

Tom had heard about Proud Pirate, the stallion that had been born in Wild River Canyon. Of all the wild horses he was judged the most fearless.

Like a red-brown flash the stallion would rush up to a herd of tame ranch horses. Biting and kicking, he would choose the horses he wanted to join his own herds.

Then he would lead them off to his faraway hills. No cowboy had ever been able to come anywhere near Proud Pirate.

He made trouble for all the ranchers in North Texas. They all wanted to catch and tame him. One of the ranchers, Mr. Hall, had offered two prize steers to any cowboy who could rope Pirate.

When Proud Pirate was just a long-legged young horse, he had seen his mother roped. She had been taken away, kicking and biting.

This had made the wild stallion watchful of men. And he was smart—much smarter, in fact, than most horses. He was braver, too, and as swift as if he had winged hoofs.

Thinking of the stallion, Jim began to swing his rope swiftly. "I'm glad Proud Pirate is back," he said. "I'm going to win those prize steers!"

His words made the other cowboys laugh.

But Jim had studied how the stallion acted. He thought Proud Pirate would head for Wild River Canyon tonight.

Tom was wakeful that night. Often he imagined he heard the thunder of the stallion's hoofbeats. In the distance he heard a wild horse neigh. This started the ranch horses neighing and kicking.

It seemed only a moment later that Jim shook him. "Wake up, sleepyhead," he said. "I'm going after Proud Pirate. You can come along."

Quickly Tom put on his cowboy boots and mounted his pony. He followed Jim out to the wet grass that grew along Wild River. In the distance they saw something moving.

"Sh-h-h-h! It's Proud Pirate and his herd," Jim whispered. "We'll circle around so that they can't get our smell."

Tom's heart beat fast. Riding quietly, he and Jim soon reached the foot of the canyon.

They got off their horses. Frightened neighs and thundering hoofs sounded above them.

"That's Pirate's call of warning to his herd," Jim whispered.

Again and again they heard the excited neighs and the kicking hoofs. Tom was scared. He wanted to run away. But if he did, Jim would make fun of him.

By now it was almost daylight. Tom saw something moving on the rocky ledge above.

"It's Pirate!" exclaimed Jim. "We're blocking his way out of the canyon."

Now they could see the big stallion picking his way carefully along the ledge. A patch of sunlight splashed his smooth red-brown coat.

"What a beauty!" whispered Jim.

By this time the horse had reached a long narrow shelf that stretched out over the canyon. There was a drop of two hundred feet to the river bed below. Above the shelf stretched a high tower of smooth rock. This tower blocked one end of the ledge.

"The only way he can escape is to jump across the river," shouted Jim. "But he's too smart to take that chance. I'm going after him. I've got to win those steers."

No sooner had Jim spoken than he tripped and caught his foot between two rocks. "Oh!" he cried as he fell. "Oh, I've hurt my leg. I can't climb now."

Sadly Jim eyed the narrow ledge where Proud Pirate was racing up and down, neighing and kicking!

Suddenly a thought flashed into Tom's mind. Here was his chance to prove to Jim that he was no baby. Here was his chance to prove that he, too, could use a rope.

"Jim, lend me your rope," Tom begged. "I'll go up and try to rope Pirate."

"You?" Jim chuckled at his young brother. "A baby like you!"

"Please let me try," Tom begged.

"Well, all right," Jim finally agreed. He handed Tom the rope.

Five minutes later Tom was halfway up the steep hill. After that, the going got harder.

Now he was puffing for breath as he climbed. He could see Proud Pirate watching him from above. The stallion's wise brown eyes were fixed on the much-feared rope that was hanging across the boy's shoulder.

Just as Tom stepped onto the ledge, the stallion rushed to the open end above the river. With a toss of his head, he stopped. He showed his teeth. His hoofs pawed the ground.

"Rope him, cowboy," Jim shouted.

Tom smiled. "Cowboy," Jim had called him. Tom was no longer a baby, but a cowboy trying his best to rope a wild stallion.

Tom began to swing the rope. He gave it a swift toss. It swished through the air, circling one of the stallion's kicking legs. Tom caught his breath as the rope stretched.

Suddenly his hands burned. The rope was being pulled out of his hands! It was gone!

Suddenly Tom saw Proud Pirate leap into the air, the free rope-end trailing behind him. For a moment the stallion's body seemed to hang in the air. Then his front hoofs hit the ground on the other side of the canyon. His back legs pushed to get a hold.

Tom held his breath. If Pirate fell to the river bed below . . . ! But no, he had made it safely. Tossing his head, he galloped off.

Tom was glad Pirate had escaped! He thought such a brave, beautiful animal should be free. Now Pirate could go his proud, swift way, the untamed King of the Range.

Back at camp, Jim told everyone what had happened. "Tom wins the steers!" he said.

Mr. Hall agreed. "Pirate's too wise to come back now that he has felt the rope," he said. "He won't disturb our herd again."

What Do You Think?   Interpreting character

How did Tom feel when Jim called him "Cowboy"?
When he roped Proud Pirate?
When Proud Pirate escaped?

Singing Cloud

The Navaho Indians believe that winter is the best season for telling the old tales.

"During the winter months," the Navahos insist, "the snakes and the thunder are sleeping. They cannot hear the secrets that the wise old men tell in the tales."

One winter day, when the snakes and the thunder should have been sleeping, a Navaho boy went into the desert. The name of the boy was Singing Cloud.

Singing Cloud had promised to watch his mother's sheep while they searched for grass.

It was a perfect day. The sky was as blue as the blue stone earrings in the little Navaho's brown ears.

Just one juniper tree rose out of the stony desert. In the hot summer months it made a cool spot where Singing Cloud might rest. When the freezing time came, its berries dropped to the ground.

Today Singing Cloud was surprised to see a bright green handkerchief hanging from a branch. "The juniper tree is waving the handkerchief to me," he whispered to himself.

He left the sheep and the lambs feeding on the desert grass. Swiftly he climbed into the branches of the tree.

"What do you have for me today, juniper tree?" he laughed. "Is this for me to tie around my head? Thank you, juniper tree!"

He took the handkerchief and held it for a moment in his hands. How beautiful the green looked against his dark skin! Then he tied the handkerchief around his head.

The moment the handkerchief made a circle around his hair, something magic happened. He did not know why it happened. He only knew that he felt very happy.

He began to sing:

"I am walking in the morning.
I hear the bluebird calling.
I hear the water flowing,
The Old Age River flowing."

The more he sang, the happier he became. He forgot the sheep and lambs. He watched the smoke that rose from the houses of his village. He felt there was magic in the smoke drifting lazily from the hogans that looked like great beehives on the desert.

The smoke which was now puffing out of his mother's hogan seemed unlike any other smoke. The puffs seemed to take the shapes of brown-skinned dancers.

246

Singing Cloud sat in the juniper tree and watched the smoke taking shape before his eyes. He imagined he saw two rows of Navaho men facing each other and dancing. Their long, black hair was hanging over their backs. Yellow fox skins hit against their legs as they danced.

All the men held rattles and shook them as they danced and sang. They were singing a well-known Navaho song, one that Singing Cloud had often heard.

The song was about a poor Navaho boy of long ago. In those far-off ages he had made a boat out of a hollow log. One morning, just at dawn, he had climbed into his boat and drifted down the Old Age River.

Going down the river was a brave thing for a Navaho to do, Singing Cloud thought. Desert people know little about boats.

As he watched the dancers and listened to the rattles, Singing Cloud longed to do a brave thing, too.

Suddenly the wind blew the handkerchief away and dropped it on a lamb's back. All the sheep became frightened and ran.

Singing Cloud hurried down from the juniper tree. He ran after his handkerchief, for the minute it left his head the magic went with it. He no longer heard songs or saw dancers. He saw only frightened sheep and lambs running in every direction.

He picked up his handkerchief and folded it into a band. He tied the band around his head. As soon as it touched his hair, he felt happier, and the magic returned. Now he was able to gather the flock together.

On the way to the sheepfold, his sister, Bright Dawn, ran up to him. She noticed the handkerchief that circled his smooth black hair.

"It's pretty," Bright Dawn said. "I'd like to know where you found it."

"Hanging in the juniper tree," replied the boy. "It's magic. It makes me want to do something brave, as if I were a great chief."

"But you are not a chief," said Bright Dawn. "You are only a herder of sheep."

"There could be something brave in my head," said the boy. Then he added, "I'd like to know why you came to meet me."

"A rattlesnake is sleeping on your sheepskin in the hogan," she replied.

The boy trembled. "I'd be glad if you would put the sheep and the lambs in the fold," he said. "Now I have something brave to do."

Slowly he entered the hogan. No one was there but his small baby cousin who was sleeping. She was in danger if anything disturbed the rattlesnake.

Fear made it hard for Singing Cloud to think clearly. So he sang, "I am walking in the morning. In beauty I am walking."

Singing Cloud wondered how he could take the snake from the hogan. As he looked around, he saw a stick lying in the corner. It was the stick his mother used to weave the woolen blankets all Navaho women make.

He picked up the weaving stick. "Be a good stick," he said. "Help me touch the rattlesnake without waking it. Help me carry it away."

To the sleeping snake he sang, "I am walking in the morning. You are sleeping in the morning. Young chief, it is time to return to your home in the earth."

Then Singing Cloud placed the stick under the snake and carried it out of the hogan.

As he set the snake down, he whispered, "Go away, young chief. Don't enter the hogan again." The snake woke up and crawled away.

Singing Cloud took the weaving stick back into the hogan. He touched the handkerchief folded around his head and smiled. He felt happier than ever before. He felt like a chief, for today he had done a brave thing.

A Rope Around the Sun

Once upon a time there were only Indians living in our country. The many tribes of Indians lived in different ways.

The tribes in the East lived in the forests. So did the Winnebagos, although their homes were near the Great Lakes.

In the Middle West lived the Plains Indians in their tepees. These tribes hunted the great herds of buffalo that lived on the prairies.

In the Southwest lived the Navahos in their hogans shaped like beehives.

Near the Navahos there was a tribe that lived on the cliffs above the canyons. Their houses were cut out of rock walls and reached high up the sides of the cliffs. To enter a house a person had to climb onto its roof. Then he descended through an opening.

In each village on the cliffs there was a large meeting room. To enter this room, too, the Indians had to climb onto the roof and descend through an opening.

Inside the round meeting room, a fire of juniper logs burned in the middle of the floor. Beside the fire sat the wise men of the tribe. They sang songs and told stories.

Around the walls sat children of all ages. They listened eagerly to the wise men.

The men told stories to explain why the world is the way it is. They explained the thunder and the moon and the stars. They explained the animals, too, and told why each one was different—some wild, some gentle.

Why do some animals have claws? Why do others have strange shapes? The wise men gave the answers in stories they handed down through the ages.

One favorite story tells about a strange, gentle animal, the mole. It explains why the mole chooses to live in the cool, dark earth.

Once there was a little Indian boy named Shooter of Birds. He could shoot his bow and arrow better than any other boy on the cliff.

One day his mother made him a coat of birds' feathers. The feathers of the robin, the bluebird, the crow, and other birds went into the making of this coat.

Shooter of Birds put on his coat. He took his bow and arrow and descended the path into the canyon. There he went hunting.

But the sun shone so hotly upon him that Shooter of Birds became angry. He shook his bow and arrow at the sun and cried, "I'll shoot my arrow through you, Old Sun."

But the sun only laughed merrily.

Then Shooter of Birds became angrier than ever. "I'll catch you in a trap," he cried.

Shooter of Birds took several very strong ropes and made a trap. Then he said, "I'll climb the narrow path that leads to the highest mountain and trap the sun."

He climbed to the top of the mountain, and there he set his trap.

Now, Old Sun could not see the trap. He continued on his path across the sky. After several hours, he rolled straight into the trap. The sun pulled and kicked, but he was held so fast he could not escape.

Then it grew dark on the earth. Birds flew into their nests and gently folded their wings.

People said, "Wait until morning draws near. Light will come with the dawn."

But there was no dawn because the sun did not continue on his way.

In the morning the Indians on the cliff cried, "Where is the warm sun? There is no heat on the earth. We are cold."

The birds in their nests cried, "We are trembling from the cold. We shall freeze."

The trees and the flowers that grew on the cliff cried, "We cannot live without the sun's heat and light. Our roots will freeze!"

Shooter of Birds laughed, "Yesterday the heat from the sun burned my skin. So I set a trap and caught him in it."

"And now all living things are freezing!" cried the angry people. "How shall we free the sun? Someone must climb the mountain and break the rope that has trapped him."

The hawk, who was chief of the birds, spoke up. "If I lead the way," he said, "who will follow me up the mountain path?"

"I," cried all the birds.

"I," cried the coyote and the other animals.

The crickets, the grasshoppers, and all the other insects decided to go, too.

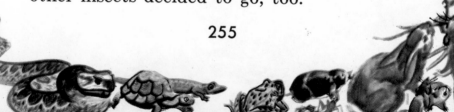

Then all the birds flew out of their nests. They took their places behind the hawk.

After them came the coyote and the other animals. There were big, strong animals, like the wolf and the bear. There were small, gentle animals, too, such as the rabbit, the turtle, and the mole. Behind them crept the cricket and the other insects.

Slowly this brave company began to creep up the mountain path. Finally, after traveling for several days, they saw a light ahead of them. It was the sun.

On they crept. But the closer they crept to the sun, the stronger was his light.

"The light makes our eyes smart," cried the birds, folding their wings over their eyes.

The coyotes and the wolves began to growl. Their growling scared many of the smaller, gentler animals. Some turned back and descended the mountain.

The others continued on their way. But at last the hawk said, "It's no use. We shall become blind if we go any nearer the sun."

Then all but the gentle mole turned back. The mole crept on, up the mountain path. The sun grew hotter than red-hot coals. Its heat was hard to bear. Its rays became blinding. But that did not stop the mole. He knew the world needed the sun.

Inch by inch the mole crept on. Although the sun's rays nearly blinded him, he crept right up to the trap. He chewed the rope until the sun was free.

How joyful the animals and the people were to see the rays of the sun again! How glad they were to feel its heat once more!

The poor mole was almost blind, and so have all moles been ever since. They live in tunnels in the dark, cool earth. To this day all animals remember the wonderful way their friend, the mole, set the sun free.

Spotless Smith, the Cowboy

Spotless Smith was the kind of cowboy who delighted the eyes of people from the East.

Spotless worked on Golden Arrow Ranch. Even when he rounded up the cattle, Spotless dressed in fancy clothes. His jackets were often made of silk, and his white hat was almost two feet wide. He always tied a bright silk handkerchief around his neck. His boots shone like jewels.

His whip was fancy, too. Its handle was striped with silver. The silver shone brightly enough to blind a person.

Spotless was a smart-looking sight on horseback. His Spanish saddle glittered with all the colors of the rainbow. Even when he rode alone, he looked like a parade.

258

Spotless talked as big and as fancy as he looked. If you told a tall tale, he invented one that was much taller. He loved to boast of his adventures with deadly coyotes and mountain lions. He fancied himself to be a hero.

Once another cowboy, who was called Bullet Bangs, said to Spotless, "Just now I met a five-foot rattlesnake. This rattler was stretched across the path. But I sent a bullet through the middle of its head."

Spotless boasted, without batting an eye, "Snakes don't scare me. Once I came across a rattler ten feet long. I just tamed him. For months I used this live snake as a riding whip. But I wanted something prettier, so I bought this fancy whip with the silver-striped handle."

Little by little, Spotless became famous in the West. All the ranchmen knew about his boasting. They called him "Spotless Smith, the boastful cowboy."

One day Spotless was talking with Bullet Bangs and three other fellows from the Golden Arrow Ranch. These other three cowboys were Coyote Bill, Drippy Stoner, and Cranberry Jones.

The five cowboys were good friends. They kept close to one another when they worked on the range. At night they had bunks next to one another in the bunkhouse.

At this moment they were leaning against the wire fence outside the bunkhouse. They were telling tall tales. Those that Spotless told about his adventures were taller than all the others put together.

Spotless was in the middle of describing to the fellows how he had just whipped a wild mountain lion.

But suddenly Cranberry interrupted.

"What's the matter with Little Helper?" said Cranberry, shading his eyes. "Look at him! He acts as if a fifteen-foot snake were chasing him."

Little Helper was nine years of age and did small jobs on the ranch.

At this moment he was racing toward the cowboys. His hair stood on end, and he was taking seven feet to the jump. His mouth was moving, but not a word came out.

Little Helper came to a stop where the cowboys were standing. When he could find his voice, he almost howled like a coyote.

"There's a skunk in the bunkhouse!" he howled. "There's a skunk in . . . ."

"A skunk!" interrupted the men, leaning toward him. "A skunk in *our* bunkhouse?"

"He's a big skunk," howled Little Helper. "I don't want to mix with him."

"I suggest that we send a dog in search of the skunk," said Bullet Bangs. "In fact, I'll send mine."

261

"No!" interrupted Coyote Bill. "Your dog would growl and make the skunk angry. Then the skunk would make the bunkhouse smell. You know how a skunk acts when he's disturbed or angry."

Then Drippy Stoner spoke. "I suggest that we build a fire and smoke that skunk out."

Bullet Bangs moaned, "If I could only get my gun out of the bunkhouse, I'd shoot that animal. I have no taste for skunks."

Coyote Bill cried, "I don't agree! Never shoot a skunk. That's as bad as chasing a skunk with a dog. I've heard that ever since I was born."

"What else can we do?" asked Drippy in a desperate voice. "Our best clothes are in the lockers in the bunkhouse. And we need them to wear to the barn dance Friday night. What a mix-up!"

Now Spotless Smith had sat in silence listening to everyone. He just sat there looking like a perfect gentleman in those fancy clothes of his.

But finally he said, "Gentlemen, there's no need to feel desperate. I suggest you let me remove the skunk. I intend to show you the only way it can be done."

"How do you intend to remove the skunk?" inquired the others eagerly.

"It's easy," said Spotless. "To remove a skunk, pick him up gently by his tail. As long as you hold him gently by the tail, he can't do anything terrible."

"I still insist a skunk is a skunk, no matter how you hold him," growled Cranberry. "And besides . . . ."

"Fellows," interrupted Spotless, "I know what I'm saying. I've handled rattlers, howling coyotes, and other terrible animals. Once I tamed twenty-seven Mississippi mud turtles. I'm famous for such jobs."

Then Spotless walked into the bunkhouse.

"See, it can be done with ease!" boasted the cowboy, carrying out the skunk by the tail. "This way he's harmless as a lamb."

"How will you set the skunk free?" asked Cranberry. "That won't be easy."

"Why, uh . . . I . . . ," growled Spotless. "I never did hear how to set a skunk free."

"That skunk is terribly angry," chuckled Drippy Stoner. "The minute his feet touch the ground he intends to do something about the way you have been handling him."

Spotless Smith, the boastful cowboy, sat down on a box. A desperate look crept over his face. He was still holding the skunk by the tail when the other cowboys rode off.

He may be sitting there still!

What Do You Think? Figurative language

Say It Another Way

"glittered with all the colors of the rainbow"

"he looked like a parade"

"acts as if a fifteen-foot snake were chasing him"

"harmless as a lamb"

The Mischief Maker

On the desert lived a rat that worked at a strange trade. When he saw something pretty, he would drop what he was carrying and would pick up the new thing instead. This way he traded one thing for another.

So this smart little rat was called Trader Rat, although sometimes he was called Pack Rat. He got his name because it was his habit to pack or carry heavy things.

Trader was a fine-looking fellow, with thick fur as soft as silk. He had sharp teeth, large ears, and a long, thick tail. He looked like a small rabbit who had started out to be a squirrel and changed his mind.

Trader had built his nest down in the sandy desert below a cactus bush. It was his habit to cover the openings of his nest with fallen cactus branches. The sharp cactus kept other animals away from the nest.

He stored grass and other desert food in his nest. He had a large collection of sticks and stones, too, as well as many other things he had carried home.

Trader Rat slept during the daytime. He traded at night when the moon flooded the cool desert with its silver light.

One night Trader heard the sharp cry of a coyote. He began to run for dear life. Leaving the coyote far behind, he found himself in a part of the desert he had never seen before. Right before him stretched a Very Big Thing. It was a house trailer.

Lying near the trailer were all kinds of handsome treasures that had belonged to the people who lived inside. Trader stared with greedy eyes.

There were old knives, tin cans, and broken clay bowls. Trader thought they would make a handsome collection.

"Oh, what a wonderful place!" Trader Rat thought. Weaving in and out, he searched eagerly for the prettiest things there. He intended to pack them home to his nest.

"Some creatures are careless with their treasures," Trader Rat thought.

In the middle of the pile the hawk-eyed creature found something special. It was shiny, and it had a round fat face.

"How handsome!" Trader thought. "If that were mine, it would be like having my own moon."

Trader's moon was an old alarm clock. It was too heavy for him to lift. So he pushed it. As his teeth banged against the alarm, a loud ring broke the silence.

The noise made Trader Rat run for cover. He thought the strange thing might chase him. When it didn't, Trader grew bold. He crept near the alarm clock. He wanted it so much that he became even bolder.

Soon he was pushing and poking with all his might. Still it was no use. Then he had an idea. Since he could not move the thing to his old home, he would build himself a new nest around it.

Trader had never worked so hard. By dawn he had piled sticks and stones and pieces of cactus a foot high all over the alarm clock.

That evening he searched for food in a big can beside the trailer. He dined on bread and tasty vegetables. Then he had a little piece of cake before he settled down for the night.

Trader had never seen the people who lived in the trailer. It was his habit to sleep during the daytime when they were about.

One night, however, Trader grew so bold that he went into the cabin next door to the trailer. The grandfather of the trailer family, old Mr. Stover, lived there alone.

Beside the fireplace in Grandfather Stover's cabin was a pile of sticks. These sticks were just the right shape for the roof of Trader's nest.

True to his old habits, Trader carried the sticks to his nest. On each trip back to the cabin he left something else from his collection to replace the sticks he had taken.

Early next morning, before dawn, old Grandfather Stover got up. He intended to build a fire. First he began to tear up some paper. Then he reached for a stick of wood.

Oh, how he howled! He howled and growled. Instead of firewood, he had picked up a cactus branch Trader had put there.

Poor Grandfather! He must have had twenty cactus needles in his hand! All morning Billy and Mary, who lived in the trailer, pulled out the sharp needles.

Who did it? Grandfather thought Billy had done it for a joke. But Billy said he wouldn't even touch a cactus plant!

The next night Trader was so bold that he went into the trailer. What a time he had! He found a clay bowl of berries on the table. He carried them to his nest and hurried back to refill the bowl with orange skins.

How upset Mother was next morning! She was sure the children had done the mischief and had put the orange skins into the bowl.

But Billy and Mary said they didn't know a thing about it.

That night Trader went back to the trailer. He sniffed around and knocked over a tin can of tea. It fell with a bang.

Mother cried in alarm, "What's that?"

Father answered, "Just the wind!"

In the morning, Mother was more angry than ever. There on the floor lay a line of nails, reaching from Father's tool box to the door. There was not a tea ball in the house!

"The wind!" Mother exclaimed. But what else could it be?

"Maybe it's ghosts," said Grandfather.

"I'd say it's elves," suggested Mary.

"It's surely funny," said Father.

"I saw a line of footprints on the desert sand that looked like a rat's," said Billy.

"No rat can get the best of me!" Mother boasted. "I'm sick of this bold mischief maker. Sticking Grandfather's hand with cactus needles! Taking nails out of the tool box! Tonight I'm going to trap it. You may all sleep, but I'm going to wait up for that creature."

271

That night Mother heard Trader rustling over the floor. She turned on the light. Then she took a switch and went after him.

Trader jumped from a chest of drawers. She chased him under the bed. But the switch never once touched him.

At last Mother opened the trailer door, and Trader made a beeline for his nest.

"I don't know what kind of a creature it is," Mother said. "It's either a rabbit or a rat. But either he stays away, or we move!"

"He was on the desert first," Grandfather laughed. "I think we had better move!"

First they cleaned the trailer, throwing more things away. After they left, Trader sniffed around, looking for things to add to his collection. He found old tools, a bright bell, eyeglasses, and a mouth organ.

Choosing the prettiest treasures, Trader put them with the wonderful alarm clock. He would never forget that fine trailer family. And they would never forget him either!

Study Pages

Accented and Unaccented Syllables

You know a number of first syllables that are likely to be unaccented. Look at the following words and quickly decide which ones have unaccented first syllables.

insist	eager	express	kicking
cattle	intend	chuckle	depend
stocking	descend	fellow	easy

Next, look at the accented second syllables of those words. Which rule below do you use to say each vowel sound?

1. One vowel, short sound, like **whip**
2. Two vowels side by side, long sound of first vowel, like **lean**
3. Two vowels, first vowel long and final silent **e,** like **age**

Now go back and look at each word with an accented first syllable. Tell which rule you use to say the vowel sound in the first syllable of each one.

Unaccented Last Syllables

You know that many words have <u>accented</u> last syllables, as **alarm** and **descend.**

A great number of words, however, have <u>unaccented</u> last syllables, as **cattle** and **stocking.** More words with different kinds of unaccented last syllables are listed below.

LAST SYLLABLE	KEY WORD	OTHER WORDS
er	eager	either, juniper
or	color	motor, harbor
en	even	chicken, garden
le	needle	gentle, handle
y	lady	fancy, berry
ow	pillow	fellow, arrow

When you see one of the above syllables at the end of a word, you know it is unaccented. Then you will know the sound, too.

Find a word above that is:
>   something used with a bow, by Indians
>   fruit picked from a bush, often tiny and round
>   a kind of tree, often seen on a desert
>   part of a hammer or of a saw

Words from Other Languages

Many of our words came from other languages, older than ours. Here are three of them.

Telephone

Tele means "far away" or "at a distance." **Phone** means "sound." So, **telephone** means "sound far away."

Before man knew about history, his hearing was only as good as his ears. After Mr. Bell invented the first electric telephone, man's voice could be heard from far away. When the radio telephone was invented, voices could be heard around the world—without wires!

Television

Vision means "seeing." **Tele** means "far away." **Television** means "seeing far away."

Long, long ago man's vision was only as good as his eyes. Later, many people were helped to see with glasses. Now, television helps us to see plays, games, and other events that take place far away.

Telegraph

Graph means "writing." So **telegraph** means "writing at a ＿＿＿."   table   distance

Vowel Sounds and Unaccented Syllables

VOWEL SOUNDS IN ACCENTED SYLLABLES	UNACCENTED LAST SYLLABLES	NEW WORDS
ir with the sound of **ear** in **fear**	**or** of **motor**	mirror
ou with the sound of **o** in **bold**	**er** of **either**	boulder
a in **act**	**er** of **either**	rather
i in **thin**	**le** of **handle**	jingle
o in **bold**	**y** of **lady**	Tony
i in **sick**	**en** of **chicken**	written

When you want to see your face as others see it, look in a ____ .

When you want to write a story about a boy, use the name ____ .

When you ring a tiny bell, you will hear a ____ .

When you need a big stone with which to stop up a hole in a fence, use a ____ .

West of the Rockies

Far-off Places

Ricardo lived in a log house, high up in the mountains, near the top of Rita Pass. He had been born in Mexico, but he had come here to live when he was little.

Behind his house a steep path went up to the highway. In front of the house another steep path descended into a canyon.

Most boys Ricardo's age would have thought it a lonely place to live. But Ricardo was never lonely. How could anyone be lonely when there were so many interesting things going on in Rita Pass?

Trains ran through there night and day. Long express trains with baggage cars crawled up the pass. One locomotive pulled in front, and two more locomotives pushed from behind.

At night, too, Ricardo liked to hear the locomotives thundering through the pass.

It was Ricardo's habit to awaken at the moment when a lighted passenger coach was below his window. Then he would see all the people going to far-off places. He had seen the names of these places on the maps in his geography book. Whenever he studied his geography, he dreamed of going away, too.

Ricardo dreamed of far-away Maine, and of the bluegrass country of Kentucky. Best of all, he liked to dream of the great Father of Waters, the Mississippi River.

Ricardo had another dream. He intended to become an engineer on a locomotive. But he would have to wait many years for that dream to come true. He must study more than geography to become an engineer.

Meanwhile, Ricardo helped his father on Saturdays. His father was hired to watch the tracks. He had a very important job, even if it did not take him to far-off places.

Ricardo was always glad when it was Saturday. Then he and his father rode up and down the tracks on a speeder, looking for broken railroad ties and for bad spikes.

Sometimes they found loose spikes. If they did not replace the loose spikes with new ones, there might be a train wreck.

When Ricardo and his father found a tie that was no longer safe, the father pulled out the loose spikes. Next they shoveled away the clay and the gravel so they could slip the tie from under the track.

Then they took a new tie from the speeder. It was not easy to slip it under the tracks and bed it down into the clay and gravel. But after it was done, there would be no wreck.

Sometimes, before Ricardo's father could drive in the new spikes, they would hear the sound of the locomotive whistle. They would quickly draw the little speeder off the track onto the gravel. Then they would wait for the great thundering locomotive to pass.

On their way home, Ricardo always noticed a boulder on the ledge.

"When the rains come," said Ricardo, "that boulder could break loose from the ledge. It could make mischief on the tracks."

His father replied, "Don't be alarmed. That boulder must have deep roots. It will remain on the ledge for ages."

The rains came late that winter in California. Sharp winds blew dark clouds across the sky. How the rain fell! Desperate ranchers began to fear for their crops.

Ricardo's father sat cozily by the fire. "It's a terrible storm," he said as the wind moaned. "The radio says it's the worst one California has had in twenty years."

The terrible storm lasted for many hours. The wind shrieked down the pass. It banged the doors and windows. It knocked down the juniper trees and the electric wires. Ricardo and his family had to use candles that night.

During the night the howling blasts that whipped around the house woke Ricardo. He could hardly see the lighted passenger coaches through the sheets of rain.

Ricardo was unable to get back to sleep until he heard the shriek of the locomotive whistle in the distance.

In the morning all the juniper trees in Ricardo's yard lay on their sides. The path to school flowed like a stream. So he had a holiday and helped his father.

278

During the several weeks of rain which followed, Ricardo worried about the boulder.

"That boulder beside the path is big enough to wreck a train," he said.

"Yes," Ricardo's father agreed, "but it has been there for years. Let us lock our speeder in the tool house. Then we can go home to our warm fire."

After dinner that night, Ricardo went to bed, but he was uneasy. The wind howled and blew in fierce blasts. The rain beat on the roof and whipped against the window shutters.

Just before twelve o'clock, Ricardo could stand it no longer. He slipped out of the house into the blasts of fierce, howling wind.

"I can't sleep until I see the boulder and make sure it's safe," he told himself.

He reached the ledge where the boulder had stood, but it was gone! The rain had stopped. In the moonlight he discovered the boulder lying on the tracks.

Ricardo wanted to go back and wake his father, but he could not take the chance. In a moment the late express would speed down Rita Pass. Besides, it would take several men to lift the great boulder.

Suddenly Ricardo had an idea. Hurrying down the path to the tracks, he reached the tool house. He opened the door with the key he always carried. Inside he searched for a signal flare. Then with the flare in his hand, he slipped along the wet clay and gravel.

Now he heard the shriek of the locomotive. It was coming through Rita Pass. With his knife Ricardo cut the top off the signal flare. Then he threw it straight as an arrow. A fierce, blinding flame lighted the canyon walls with dancing shapes.

The locomotive shrieked a warning as it slowed down and came to a stop.

Men jumped off the train. The chief engineer saw the boulder and ordered the trainmen to remove it. Then he said, "I wonder who threw that warning flare."

Ricardo took a deep breath. "I threw it," he said shyly. "I discovered the boulder on the tracks and got the flare."

"You saved many lives tonight," the engineer said. "You are one of California's heroes!"

"I love locomotives!" Ricardo answered. "When I grow up, I want to be an engineer, too. Then I will be able to travel to all the places I've seen on my geography map."

"You shall receive a free ticket to visit your favorite place now!" the engineer promised.

"I'd like to see the Mississippi River," Ricardo said.

"You will!" the engineer replied. "And many places beyond the Mississippi."

And then all the passengers gave a cheer for the boy who had saved their lives!

The Wonderful Saw

Everybody on Frog Island knows me. I'm Mr. J. J. Jones. And everybody on the island knows what happened here two years ago. I see you're a stranger in these parts. So I'd like to tell you an interesting story.

It was circus time, and men had come around to post big, colorful signs of Jingle's Circus. They put posters on walls and on barns.

No one was more excited about the circus than B Good. He was the smart red-haired fellow I hired to help me in the yard.

"Mr. Jones," B Good inquired, "what do you enjoy most in the circus parade?"

"My chief interest is the band," I replied.

I didn't want B Good to guess how much I would enjoy playing in the band.

Every day B Good inquired, "Will they really have elephants in the parade?"

"Of course," I told him, "and I'll see if they will let you lead a tame elephant."

The evening before the parade, we had a terrible electric storm. It thundered like a thousand carloads of coal being spilled onto the sidewalk.

Suddenly a fierce wind came up, whistling and howling. It made the trees bend to their roots. All night the thunder roared.

By morning the sky cleared. B Good and I brushed our hair, put on gay neckties, and started out to see the parade.

At a bend in the road, we passed a little old man driving a shiny black car. Behind the car was a shiny white trailer with green shutters. A gay poster on the trailer read: "Silverwand's Repair Shop. Things Beyond Repair Can Be Fixed. But Chiefly Toys."

"He looks like a fine person," said B Good, waving gaily to the stranger.

When we reached town, we noticed that many trees had been blown down and were lying in the streets.

"Now there won't be any parade," cried B Good as we started to walk uptown. "I won't be able to lead an elephant."

Just then a rather fat man, wearing a gay and fancy suit, approached us. A nearby policeman told us that he was Mr. Jingle, who owned the circus.

Mr. Jingle looked half mad with worry.

"These streets are covered with trees!" he said. "And I've promised the children the biggest parade ever."

I was very polite and took off my hat. "Mr. Jingle," I said with a polite nod, "of course, promises made to children should be kept. What will you give me to clean up this street? I'd enjoy doing it."

Mr. Jingle was rather surprised. Then I whispered in his ear. He nodded. "Agreed," he chuckled, "but what's your plan, Jones?"

I whispered again. "Rather a large order, but we'll take the chance," he said.

So B Good and I hopped into the car and headed for my farm. We got a cross-cut saw from my tool chest and returned to town.

We set to work on the first tree lying across Weaver Street. We puffed and grunted as we sawed at that tree. It wasn't easy work, of course, but we did our best.

A crowd gathered to watch. I thought my plan was working perfectly.

"We'll surely see that parade," I said. B Good nodded his head.

So we sawed back and forth, pushing and pulling madly. Not one of the folks offered to help, and I was angry. "Why don't a bunch of you lazy creatures help?" I shouted.

But everyone just stood with folded arms and continued to stare at me. So I climbed up on a tree trunk. "Folks," I growled, not very politely, "you'll all be able to see the parade if you stop staring and lend a hand!"

Some of the folks said sawing was too hard on their hands. Others said it hurt their necks. Still others said they had promised their wives to go shopping. Everyone had excuses. And thin excuses, too!

So B Good and I whipped off our coats. We felt as if we were roasting from the heat. We puffed and grunted some more, and sawed another trunk. Back and forth went the saw. Swish, swish, swish. Then snap! Off came a handle. It was beyond repair. I wanted to howl out loud.

I gave B Good a quarter to buy a new handle. In several minutes he was back, but there was not a tool handle to be had.

B Good told me that he had seen Mr. Silverwand in his trailer. Mr. Silverwand was fixing toys and telling gay stories to a crowd of children.

B Good had shown him the snapped-off saw handle. But Mr. Silverwand made excuses by saying, "I'd rather fix broken toys for children."

That made me terribly angry. "The silly goose, spending his time on toys," I snapped. "I'll favor him with a piece of my mind."

So we hurried to the trailer. There was Mr. Silverwand fixing a doll's broken head and telling stories.

"What do you want, Jones?" he grunted.

I told him politely that my saw handle had snapped off and I needed a new one.

"Sorry, I need my saw handles," he said.

"But the children won't see the circus parade!" B Good cried.

"The children must not miss the parade," Mr. Silverwand said with a change of heart. "I'll take a chance and lend you saw handles from my very special collection. But use the saw only on trees that are blocking the street where the parade will pass."

B Good and I hurried back to Weaver Street. Did that saw run smoothly! Swish, swish! It went tearing back and forth madly through a tree trunk.

Then something very strange happened. I sneezed and let go my handle. Then B Good sneezed and let go his handle. But the saw whipped back and forth, faster than ever. It worked perfectly.

Swish, swish, swish. We just touched the teeth to a branch. Then, smooth as a whistle, the saw easily did the work. Soon all the trees lying on Weaver Street were cut up.

I told B Good to lean the saw against the corner store. In the same breath I suggested that he get someone to remove the logs.

Soon he returned, leading an elephant. It was a grand sight to see that elephant use his trunk to toss those logs around.

"Help, Jones!" shrieked the storekeeper desperately. "My store is being wrecked!"

Sure enough, there was the saw tearing through his store. I pulled it out, suggesting B Good return the handles to Mr. Silverwand. "Tell him we'll see him later," I said.

Then B Good and I went to Mr. Jingle to get our pay for clearing the street. What pay it was! He let B Good ride a handsome elephant. He let me play in the band.

The parade was grand. Folks said it was easily the grandest parade they ever saw.

We looked for Mr. Silverwand to pay him for the use of his saw handles. But he had disappeared and was never seen again.

Holding Hands

Elephants walking
Along the trails

Are holding hands
By holding tails.

Trunks and tails
Are handy things

When elephants walk
In circus rings.

Elephants work
And elephants play

And elephants walk
And feel so gay.

And when they walk
On sawdust trails,

They're holding hands
By holding tails.

290

Sandy Does the Wash

Sandy Smith and his family had been traveling in a trailer. For several weeks the trailer had stood in a park on the California shore.

Many other children lived in the trailer park. Sandy's best friend was Tony, who lived two trailers away. Every day the two boys walked along the shore, swam in the ocean, or played ball.

One afternoon Sandy said, "I wish we could think of something different to do." Then he saw the family shopping cart filled with clothes ready to be washed. His mother had put the cart outside the trailer when she left for town an hour ago.

"I have an idea!" Sandy exclaimed to Tony. "Why don't we do the wash? We'd have fun, and help mother, too."

Tony liked the idea, so Sandy went into the trailer to get some money. He always kept his savings in an old jar.

"Don't forget the soap!" called Tony.

Sandy took a big yellow box down from a shelf. Then they left, pushing the cart down a gravel path to a little stone building in the trailer park. Inside, the washing and drying machines stood in a row.

"Let's use this machine," Sandy said. He opened the glass door and put in the clothes. There were blue jeans, handkerchiefs, sheets, and other things.

Next, Sandy put a quarter in the machine. At once the machine filled with water, which began to make a swishing sound.

"There are my blue jeans!" Sandy said. He could see them spinning around and around. "And there are my green and white shorts."

"We'd better put the soap in," Tony said.

Soap was supposed to be put into a small pipe that looked like a chimney.

Sandy picked up the box he had brought. He held it with both hands and let a lot of soap drop into the pipe.

"It looks good and soapy in there." Sandy looked through the glass door. He suddenly remembered his mother often said he should keep his clothes cleaner.

"We'd better use more soap," he said to Tony. "Mother says it cuts the grease. And I got grease all over my blue jeans." He shook more soap into the pipe.

"Let's watch a while now," Tony suggested.

The boys sat down and waited. Suddenly they heard a strange sound.

Slurp! The sound came from the machine. Slurp! There it was again, and Sandy's eyes grew wide at what he saw.

Slurp! Slurp! Foam was coming out of the pipe on top. Slurp! Slurp!

Tony and Sandy laughed. The foam made the machine look like a big drink from the ice cream stand. But suddenly Sandy became alarmed. Maybe it wasn't so funny. He had never seen any of the machines act this way before.

Slurp! Slurp! Slurp! The foam was shooting out still higher. Slurp! A blast of soapy foam hit the top of the room that time. Slurp! It almost hit Tony in the eye!

Foam was dripping down to the floor now, making big soapy islands all around.

"What do you suppose is the matter?" Sandy cried. "What will we do?"

"I—I suppose I'd better get Mr. Decker," Tony said, and he ran out.

Mr. Decker owned the trailer park. He fixed everything that went wrong. In a few seconds Tony was back with Mr. Decker.

"What on earth! What mischief are you boys up to now?" Mr. Decker cried.

"I don't know," Sandy said in a desperate voice. "I just put soap into the machine."

"You surely did!" Mr. Decker said. "You put enough soap in to wash the clothes of everybody in California! Well, there's nothing anybody can do now. We'll just have to wait until the machine runs down."

Mr. Decker waited in the doorway with Tony. Sandy waited on a chair. Every time the machine went slurp, slurp, Mr. Decker looked at Sandy. Sandy felt terrible.

But finally the slurps became fewer and fewer. The water began to look clear.

Mr. Decker took off his shoes. What funny, big feet he had! But Sandy was too polite and too uneasy to laugh.

"We have to let the clothes go through the machine again without any soap," Mr. Decker said. "After that, we'll put them into the drying machine."

All that took a long time. Then Mr. Decker splashed water over the floor, washing away all the islands of foam.

At last the clothes were ready and dry.

"I'm going to talk to your folks about this," Mr. Decker told Sandy.

Sandy was never so glad to get out of a place in his life! He pushed the cart full of dry clothes toward his trailer.

"I suppose I'd better go back to my own trailer now," said Tony.

"I wonder if my mother is home," said Sandy.

Sandy's mother wasn't home. He kicked off his wet shoes and sat down on a bed to read. But soon he went to sleep.

Later, when he woke up, he saw his mother and father bending over him.

"Are you sick?" Mr. Smith asked. "I know you don't like to sleep during the day."

"No, I'm all right," said Sandy. "Mother, did you see the wash all done?"

"Done? How could it be done already?" Mrs. Smith asked. "I left it in the cart. I was going to do it after supper tonight."

"I took it to the washing machine," Sandy said. "I wanted to help, but I put in too much soap."

"Sandy! Has anything happened to our clothes?" Mrs. Smith looked alarmed.

Mrs. Smith went to the shopping cart and took out some clothes. "Why, they are done already!" she exclaimed. "They look so beautiful, so clean and white. Sandy, I should let you do the wash all the time!"

"Aren't you mad at me?" Sandy asked. "Mr. Decker says he's going to tell you about all the soap we put in the machine."

"Those machines are very tricky," his mother said. "I'd rather you didn't do the wash again without me. But I'm happy it's done this time."

"Wash your hands," Mr. Smith added. "We're going to eat supper now."

Sandy went to the little washbowl in the trailer. He felt a lot better already.

Sandy turned on the water and reached out for the cake of soap. But then he pulled his hands back.

He wasn't going to use soap on his hands this evening. Not a chance of that! He had seen enough soap to last him for a long time!

What Do You Think? Interpreting humor

Why Is It Funny?

"Are you sick?" (page 297)

He wasn't going to use soap on his hands this evening. Not a chance of that! (page 298)

Little Pedro

Pedro watched his master, Don Shore, lean over the table in the large ranch kitchen. Something was being mixed in a big bowl.

Pedro could feel how excited Don was when he exclaimed, "It's my birthday cake!"

Pedro picked up his good ear, the one that made him look like a tired cactus rather than a dog. He watched Don spin happily around the room. Pedro was so happy, too, that he didn't care when Don stepped on his tail.

Suddenly a noise outside surprised Pedro. He barked as Don raced through the kitchen and out the door. Pedro followed as fast as he could. When he got outside, he stopped suddenly at the ranch house gate.

What was that fierce animal?

"It's a burro!" Don exclaimed.

Pedro didn't know what the big animal was. But he was happy to see Don joyful, so he decided he liked the creature, too.

"You'll have to give him a name," Don's father said.

Don scratched his nose as he thought about a name for his new pet.

Pedro sat down by the gatepost and scratched his nose, too.

"I know!" Don said. "I'll call him Pedro!"

When he heard his name, Pedro almost missed his nose and hit himself in the eye. He stood up and shook the dust from his tail.

"But that's your dog's name," Don's mother said.

"Well," Don replied, "Pedro is my favorite name, and my burro is my favorite pet. One can be Little Pedro, and the other, Big Pedro."

Little Pedro sat down again in the dust.

And when Don rode the new burro all day long, Little Pedro grew sad.

Little Pedro waited and waited for Don to come and play with him. He waited while Don ate his birthday supper. He kept on waiting, but Don never came. Then he started to bark.

"Don's in the barn," Mrs. Shore called to the dog.

Little Pedro hurried to the barn. Don was brushing Big Pedro's coat, trying to make it look like silk.

"Tomorrow we'll ride out to watch the cattle roundup," Don was saying to his burro.

Just then Big Pedro brayed.

"What's the matter?" Don asked.

Big Pedro brayed again and pawed the earth. He was watching Little Pedro!

Little Pedro was chasing his tail around and around. He started to growl in play.

"Stop that, Pedro!" Don exclaimed. "You're scaring my burro."

Little Pedro sat down on his tail, hard. He watched Don brush the burro. Then he thought he would like to be brushed, too. He jumped eagerly between Don and the burro.

Don pushed Little Pedro away swiftly.

The dog lay quietly on the ground. He was almost sick. Don's push had hurt a little, but the thing that hurt most was that Don didn't love him any more!

Little Pedro walked slowly out of the barn, his tail between his legs. He crawled under the back porch of the ranch house. He put his head between his paws.

302

The next day, Little Pedro had almost forgotten about the birthday burro. But then Don said, "Stay home, Little Pedro! We don't want you to ride with us." Little Pedro went back under the porch.

Sadly Little Pedro watched Don climb on the burro's back. He saw him ride through the gate and across the range toward the rocky canyons.

Late that afternoon Little Pedro saw Don ride in through the ranch house gate. He watched him put the burro in the barn.

Don brushed his burro's coat carefully. Then, without closing the barn door, he walked back to the house. He did not call or whistle to his dog.

Late that night a crash of thunder woke Little Pedro. It was the season for bad storms and even sudden floods.

As lightning flashed across the sky, Little Pedro saw the burro run out of the barn toward the gate. The burro was braying madly and running as hard as he could.

Little Pedro hurried out from under the porch. He tried to greet the burro with a warning bark, but he could not make himself heard over the noise of the storm. Little Pedro was frightened by the thunder and lightning, too, but he raced after the burro.

The burro ran faster, heading across the range, beyond which lay the deep canyons.

The thunder crashed as the storm became more fierce. Another flash of lightning filled the sky. And suddenly the countryside was as bright as day.

At that very moment Little Pedro saw the burro fall! He raced to the canyon where he had seen Big Pedro disappear.

The poor burro lay on the floor of the canyon, badly hurt from the fall.

Little Pedro barked and barked, and Big Pedro looked up at him. It was almost as if the two animals had a language all their own.

Little Pedro crawled over the thick roots at the edge of the canyon. He crawled over the stones and then slipped down the sides of the canyon. The canyon was so steep that Little Pedro fell, rolling over and over until he hit the floor of the canyon.

Big Pedro moaned. Little Pedro trembled, but he crawled to the side of the frightened burro. The wind shrieked and the thunder crashed. Heavy rain fell and the lightning flashed, but Little Pedro stayed with Big Pedro.

By morning the storm was over. Suddenly Little Pedro heard something.

"Little Pedro! Big Pedro!" Don was calling.

Little Pedro crept up the canyon wall. At the top he saw Don with his father and mother in the distance. He tried to bark a greeting, but he couldn't. He tried to run to greet his master, but he couldn't. Desperately he crawled toward Don. Then he saw Don's face light up.

Don came running, and Little Pedro turned back toward the canyon. Don looked down.

"Good, good dog!" Don cried. "You found Big Pedro."

Little Pedro fell to the ground, too tired to move. He felt Don's warm arms around him. He felt Don's happy tears fall upon his face. Little Pedro knew that Don loved him as much as Big Pedro. From now on they would all be friends together.

What Do You Think?   Main idea

Who is the hero of this story? Why?

The Princess on the Glass Hill

Once upon a time there was a man who had a field. In a shaded spot in the field stood a barn where the farmer stored his hay.

One morning in the middle of the summer, the farmer woke up and found the grass in his field eaten to its roots. It looked as if a great flock of sheep had fed there during the night. So that year there was no hay.

On the same night, the next summer, the same thing happened. The third summer, when that same night approached, the farmer called his three sons.

"This year one of you must lie in the barn and see who eats our grass," he said.

"I'll stop the one who does it!" the oldest son boasted.

When evening came, the oldest son went boldly to the barn and lay down to sleep.

In the middle of the night there was a terrible crash. The earth shook, and the barn walls trembled. The oldest son was so frightened that he hurried home and made excuses. That night all the grass was eaten.

Next summer, when the fearful night arrived, the second son puffed out his chest. He set off to the barn, lay down, and slept.

In the middle of the night, his sleep was interrupted by a crash. The earth shook, and the barn walls trembled. He, too, went home with excuses. And all the grass was eaten.

Next year Boots, the youngest son, made ready to go. His two brothers laughed, "You're a fine one to watch the grass, you lazy fellow. You have never done anything but sit cozily near the heat of the fire."

Boots entered the barn, lay down, and slept. But soon there was a crash like thunder. The earth shook all around him.

"Well," thought Boots, "if this is the worst that can happen, I can stand it."

Soon there came another crash. Loose things in the barn flew all around his ears. But he decided that if this was the worst that could happen, he could stand it.

The crash was repeated. This time Boots thought the walls were descending upon him. Then there was silence. The silence lasted until Boots heard a noise as if some creature were eating grass outside the barn.

Drawing a deep breath, Boots crept to the door and looked out. There stood a handsome horse with a brass saddle and brass trappings. He was cropping the grass under the greasewood bush. On the ground lay a brass suit such as a knight would wear.

"So you're the robber!" cried Boots.

Boots took out the box in which he carried his tools for starting a fire. He whipped out the steel and threw it over the horse. The horse at once became so tame that Boots was able to mount it. He rode off to a secret place, and there he hid the horse.

When Boots got home, he said, "I stayed in the barn all night. But I didn't see anything or hear anything, either. The grass is as thick as ever."

Next year the same thing happened. Boots was the only one brave enough to stay in the barn. Again there were great blasts and thundering. Again he saw a horse outside.

This horse was even grander than the first. Its saddle was not made of brass, but of silver. There was a knight's suit of silver, too.

As before, Boots took out his tinder box and tamed the horse by throwing his steel over the animal. Then he rode the horse to the hiding place where he kept the other one. After that, he went home.

Now, in the third year the crashing and the trembling came again, the worst of any year. The horse that cropped the grass was the grandest of them all. Its saddle was golden, and the knight's suit was of gold.

Boots tamed this horse, too, by throwing the steel from his tinder box over it. Then he hid the horse with the others.

Now, a few weeks later the king sent a written notice throughout the land. It was written in letters of gold.

The notice read, "The king promises the princess' hand to the man who can ride up the Hill of Glass.

"The princess will sit on a silken pillow on top of the hill. Three golden apples will be in her lap. The man who can ride up the hill and take the apples will win her hand."

Boots's two brothers told him that he was too lowly a fellow to take part in the contest. They themselves went. All the bold knights and princes in the land were there.

On the very top of the hill sat the beautiful fair-haired princess in a rustling silk dress.

All the knights and princes were eager to win her hand. But as soon as their horses set foot on the hill, down they slipped. Not one could go even a yard.

The hill was as smooth as a sheet of glass and as steep as a cliff. Although the horses had sharp spikes on their shoes, they would either spin around or slip and fall.

All at once a bold knight galloped up on the handsomest horse that had ever been seen. Its saddle was of brass. This knight rode up one third of the smooth glass hill.

"He could easily ride all the way up," thought the princess.

But when the knight covered a third of the distance, he turned and descended the hill.

The princess tossed a golden apple after him. The knight leaned over and picked it up. Then he galloped off so fast that no one could tell what had become of him.

The contest was held again. But no one could ride up the hill. Then a knight dressed in silver approached. The handsome silver knight rode two thirds of the distance up the smooth hill. Then he galloped down.

The princess tossed the second golden apple after him. The knight leaned over and picked it up. Then he rode off so fast that no one could tell what had become of him.

The contest was repeated. A handsome knight in gold rode swiftly up the smooth hill. He took the remaining golden apple from the princess' lap. Then he turned and rode off at full speed, out of sight in no time.

The king wanted to discover who had taken the golden apple. He ordered every man in the country to pass before him. Not one of the men could show the apple.

Finally Boots's two brothers came. The king asked them, "Does either of you know anyone else who has not come forth?"

"We have a brother," they said, "but he has not stepped beyond the fireside for many days. He could not have taken the apple."

"Let me see him, too," said the king.

So Boots was brought before the king.

The king asked him, "Have you got the golden apple? Speak out!"

"Yes," said Boots. "Here is the first, here is the second, and here is the third, too."

Then Boots threw off his old clothes and stood in his suit of gold. The king gladly gave him the princess' hand.

Of course, a feast was ordered. All the grand folk of the land came to the feast and made merry for months and months.

What Do You Think?   Indefinite terms (estimates)

Guess the Time

"One morning in the middle of the summer" (page 307)

"In the middle of the night" (page 308)

"a few weeks later" (page 311)

The Smoke Jumpers

Ray Woolworth stood by the narrow road that ran through the Oregon forest. His father, a forest ranger in a logger's jacket, sat nearby. While he waited for his fire fighters, Mr. Woolworth stared at the gray smoke hanging over Blizzard Mountain.

Ray was holding a mirror. It was a steel mirror that he always carried in his pocket. By holding it right, Ray had discovered he could flash the steel mirror anywhere.

First, Ray flashed the mirror at one of the big Oregon pines. He watched the spot of light dance gaily from needle to needle.

Then he saw his mother and his twin sister, Carol, coming out of the house. He turned the steel mirror on Carol's face.

"Stop it!" begged Carol, shutting her eyes. "You're blinding me."

Ray chuckled and turned toward his father, who continued to stare at Blizzard Mountain.

"Can your fire fighters keep the forest fire away from the road?" asked Ray.

"They are the best fire fighters in Oregon," replied Mr. Woolworth. "But if this job is too big for us, the forest rangers will send smoke jumpers."

"Smoke jumpers?" questioned Carol. "You mean the fire fighters who land by parachute from airplanes?"

Mr. Woolworth nodded. "Yes, Oregon has experimented with new ways of fighting our forest fires. The parachute jumpers have done a fine job. They have proved themselves to be real heroes."

At that moment a truck loaded with fire fighters and their tools roared up the road.

The truck slowed down just long enough for Mr. Woolworth to jump in. Then it raced on at top speed and disappeared around the bend.

As soon as the truck had disappeared, Mrs. Woolworth said to the children, "You two stay outside and play. I have work to do inside the house."

Ray nodded in the direction of a tall Oregon pine.

"Come on, Carol," he suggested eagerly. "I'll race you to that pine tree."

"No, I have on a good dress," replied Carol.

"Oh," grunted Ray, "you've always got a good dress on. You should wear overalls."

Carol walked away to get a better look at the forest fire while Ray played with his steel mirror. He was trying to flash it on a boulder when Carol called him.

"The smoke is becoming thicker!" she exclaimed. "Do you suppose the fire will creep up the valley and block the road?"

"Don't get scared," said Ray boldly. "If the trucks can't get through, the smoke jumpers will come."

"But how will they discover our tiny house here in these big pine trees?" asked Carol.

"Oh!" exclaimed Ray in alarm. "I never thought of that."

Several minutes later Mrs. Woolworth came out of the house to air some pillows. She shaded her eyes and stood staring at the smoke which clouded the valley.

"Forest fires are terrible things," she said. "Sometimes they are started by lightning. But often they are started by a careless person. This fire began only yesterday. But this autumn weather has been so dry that the pine needles burn like tinder."

"What's tinder?" interrupted Ray.

"Tinder is almost anything that catches fire from just a spark," she replied. "Pine needles make good tinder. So many of our beautiful trees will be lost in this fire!"

By noon the smell of smoke blew strong up the valley. The children's eyes were smarting and stinging from the blinding smoke. A fawn and several other woods creatures hurried by and swam across the pond.

Suddenly Ray cried out in fright, "I think the road must be shut off! The fire fighters haven't a chance of getting through."

Then Mrs. Woolworth said quietly to the children, "Help me pack some food and clothing into the suitcases. It would be wise to leave soon. We can follow the course of the stream to the lake. There we'll be safe."

The children began to pack bread, sugar, canned meat, jars of honey and jelly, and pieces of candy. Mrs. Woolworth packed their jackets and woolen stockings in case the weather turned cooler.

All at once the children heard an airplane roaring over the valley. They hurried outside.

"The airplane is coming toward us," cried Carol. "Perhaps it's a smoke jumper's airplane, but the pilot will never see us.

"Ray! You've still got your mirror, haven't you? Could you signal him with it?"

Ray's hands trembled as he flashed the steel mirror. The children held their breath.

A tiny white spot spilled out of the airplane, spread out, and became a parachute. Slowly it descended. More puffs of white drifted down through the air.

"Our signal worked!" cried Carol happily.

"The smoke jumpers are here!" Ray shouted to his mother.

They saw a parachute land next to the boulder lying just beyond their house.

"Let me help fight the fire," begged Ray.

"We'll all help!" cried Mrs. Woolworth.

When they reached the smoke jumper, he had thrown off his parachute. Now he was speaking into a small radio telephone.

When the smoke jumper snapped off his wireless telephone, Mrs. Woolworth said, "We'd like to lend a hand."

"Come on," he suggested. "You can put out the flying sparks. I'll lead the way."

They ran toward the woods, where the fire already had a head start. Sparks were flying, and big tree trunks were burning. But the smoke jumpers were there, fighting the flames with chemicals and clearing out underbrush.

Farther back, Carol, Ray, and Mrs. Woolworth were fighting sparks to keep the fire from spreading. They either beat out the sparks with wet bags or covered them with earth. They worked desperately for several hours.

Finally the smoke jumper stood up. "The danger to your house is over," he said.

Mrs. Woolworth's lips were dry from the heat of the fire. Her smarting eyes were blinded by tears brought on by the stinging smoke. The tears ran down her face.

"I hardly know how to thank you," she said. "I shall never forget how kind you've been. You've saved our belongings."

"Smoke jumpers always do the job for which they are hired," interrupted the man. "Thank the person who was wise enough to signal us with a mirror."

A proud feeling rose inside Ray. He was on the point of boasting, "The steel mirror is mine. I'm the person who signaled."

Then he happened to see his sister's tired, drawn face, red from the heat. Her hands were scratched and her nails were broken. Her clothes were splashed with mud. He stood beside her. "It was really Carol who suggested it," he said.

From Coast to Coast

Tommy Price was delighted when Mr. Wakefield suggested that he visit the offices of *The Morning Sun*. The *Sun* was one of the finest newspapers on the West Coast.

Mr. Wakefield, who was the night editor of the *Sun,* had just come to live next door to the Prices. He and Tommy had become friends while each was cutting his grass.

"May I bring my cousin, Don Bray?" Tommy asked quickly. "Don and I plan to start our own newspaper soon. We'd like to see how you run your paper."

"Tom Edison had his own newspaper when he was a boy," chuckled Mr. Wakefield. "I suppose it could happen again. So bring Don Bray along. You boys may learn a few things before you start your newspaper."

The boys entered the *Sun* offices at seven o'clock on Friday evening.

"You've come at a good time," laughed Mr. Wakefield as he greeted the boys. "We start printing at ten o'clock. When the presses roll, we say the paper is put to bed. Much of the news is already written. I'd like to show you where it's being set in type."

The boys were taken into a room filled with noisy typesetting machines. The news which the editors had sent down was written by hand or with a typewriter. It was the typesetter's job to set the news in type.

"Each typesetter works at a keyboard that has keys like those on a typewriter," said Mr. Wakefield. "Each key he hits helps to make a line of type. Many lines of type are gathered and made into a printing plate.

"Then all the plates are placed on a press. That press prints both sides of the sheet, folds, cuts, and turns it out as a finished newspaper. Thousands of copies are printed."

Don asked, "How do you ever get enough news to fill all the pages of a large newspaper? Don't you ever run short?"

"We never run short of news," said Mr. Wakefield. "We can't begin to print half of what comes in. My job is to choose the chief events that we want to use."

Mr. Wakefield explained that the number of pages for the next morning's paper had been decided upon before six o'clock.

"Look," he said. "Here is the layout for page one of tomorrow's *Sun.*" He held up a large sheet of paper. On it he had blocked out the place for each news event that would be written up in the morning paper.

"Of course," continued Mr. Wakefield, "by the time the *Sun* goes to press, this first page may look different. We change our plans to keep up with the news as it comes in."

Next, the boys visited the City Room, where the editors were busy writing or telephoning. All the editors were hurrying to get their copy in before the deadline.

Don and Tommy met the baseball editor, the radio-television editor, and the woman's page editor.

They met the children's page editor, too. She said, "You've heard of Pepperminta, the greedy Mississippi goat. We're starting an amusing continued story about her. You can begin *The Feast of the Vines* on page twenty of tomorrow's *Sun*."

The boys visited the room where news was received in different languages.

Then Mr. Wakefield said, "Now I'll show you the Teletype Room, where news is received from branch offices."

The Teletype Room was filled with pounding typewriters. But Tommy and Don had never seen such typewriters.

The keys moved up and down, and the letters printed as the hammers danced. But nobody was there to do the typewriting. It was easy to imagine that unseen ghosts sat at the machines, hammering out the news.

"Really, there's only one man doing all this typing," explained Mr. Wakefield. "To send the story, he sits in a faraway office at a master machine. Whatever he types is carried over wires to teletype machines in this office and elsewhere."

Mr. Wakefield looked at the paper in one machine. He read about an airport being built in Mexico. He read about a streamlined airplane that was flying overseas. Next came the baseball news.

"The Braves are playing the Pirates," he said. "So far it's Braves 8—Pirates 0."

"Here's some front-page news!" he said.

The boys looked over Mr. Wakefield's shoulder and read for themselves:

THE LEADING CHEMICAL ENGINEERS IN OUR COUNTRY ARE HOLDING A MEETING TONIGHT IN BUFFALO. ONE OF THEIR SPEAKERS HAS JUST STATED THAT A NEW CHEMICAL HAS BEEN DISCOVERED.

EXPERIMENTS HAVE ALREADY BEEN MADE WITH THE CHEMICAL. THESE EXPERIMENTS HAVE PROVED THE CHEMICAL MAY BE USED FOR MAKING HUNDREDS OF THINGS IN EASIER AND BETTER WAYS.

THE NEW CHEMICAL IS INTENDED FOR SUCH THINGS AS STOCKINGS, BRUSHES, TOOL HANDLES, CLOCK CASES, CAMERAS, JARS, AND BOWLS.

BEGINNING TOMORROW THE CHEMICAL WILL BE SHIPPED TO PLANTS ALL OVER THE UNITED STATES.

"That's a very big story," said Mr. Wakefield when the last words of it had come over the teletype. "I'll order it to be put on page one."

328

Then Mr. Wakefield said, "It's ten o'clock already. Soon the paper will go to press. The editors will go home. But the teletype will continue to get stories from all over the country."

"It's like the people in one big family talking at bedtime!" Tommy said.

Mr. Wakefield nodded. "Yes, Maine might say she's buried under an early blizzard. Mississippi might be afraid of a flood. Something wonderful might be happening to a person in California. Someone in Oregon might be in trouble."

Tommy could almost see the United States at work and play from coast to coast. He could almost see the cities and deserts, the canyons and mountains, the rivers and lakes. All the places that until now had been only names in his geography book.

And suddenly he felt very proud! He was proud because he knew that he, too, belonged to this great country, this family of states.

Study Pages

Learning New Words

excuses

1. In how many places do you see vowel letters?
   a. Is there a sounded vowel in each place?
   b. Then how many syllables does the word have?

2. When a word begins with **ex,** which syllable is often accented?
   a. What rule helps you know the vowel sound in the accented syllable? Say the sound of the vowel.
   b. Say the accented syllable.

3. What letters often stand for the sound of **x** in the first syllable? Say the syllable.

4. What letters stand for the last syllable? Say the word, using the sound of those letters as an unaccented syllable.

When you use **excuses,** you are trying:
   to tell why something was not done.
   to win favor for an act.

First and Last Syllables

First	MEANING	WORD	MEANING
re	again	retype	to type again
un	not	unwritten	not written
un	opposite	unfold	take the
	act		folds out

Last			
en	made of	silken	made of silk
en	to make	sweeten	to make sweet
ful	with	boastful	with boasts
y	somewhat	foamy	like foam
y	full of	greasy	full of grease
er	person who	dreamer	one who dreams
less	without	hairless	without hair
ly	in a way	politely	in a polite way

Use one of the words above in each sentence.

Jane used sugar to _ful_ her orange drink.

Before you make up your bed, you may have to _ly_ your blanket.

The cave man had an _Less_ law that the animal he trapped was his to keep.

Thanking a person who gave you a present is the way to act _ly_ at a birthday party.

Which One?

blast **1** A strong rush of wind; as, the icy *blasts* of winter. **2** A sudden rush of something. **3** The sound made by a whistle.

handle **1** To touch, feel, or move with the hand. **2** To take care of; as, to understand how to *handle* a horse. **3** That part of anything, such as a tool, that is held by the hand.

mad **1** Out of one's mind. **2** Very angry.

snap **1** To bite or try to bite something. **2** To say sharp or angry words; as, to *snap* out an order. **3** To break suddenly with a sharp noise. **4** To make a sharp noise; as a fire *snaps*. **5** To close or shut something with a sharp noise. **6** A thin cookie.

type **1** A kind or order; as, people of gentle *type*. **2** In printing, a block pressed against paper. **3** To typewrite.

How is the word used?

blast, pages 278 (blasts), 294, 310 (blasts)

handle, pages 287, 288

mad, pages 284, 298

snap, pages 286, 287 (snapped), 321 (snapped)

type, pages 324, 327 (types)

On Your Own!

You have learned enough about the sounds of consonants, vowels, and syllables to say almost any word you meet.

Here are some easy one-syllable words that you will meet in the next book. Use a vowel rule or a vowel sound you know to say each one.

wag	shed	crouch	vest
hose	tent	pain	rug
tap	shot	crack	cave

Now try some words with more than one syllable. Remember these three steps:

1. Decide how many syllables the word has.
2. Find the accented syllable and use what you know about vowel sounds to say the syllable.
3. Recall a word having the same unaccented syllable.

floated	cellar	dealer	attack
bucket	indeed	tailor	rubber

Don't forget the meanings! Which two go together?

jewel	dealer	cellar
bucket	tailor	needle
hose	rubber	cave
tail	crouch	wag

PHONIC SKILLS
AND
THINKING ABILITIES

Two types of direct and practical help are given in this section (pp. 330-353) of this storybook:

1. Introduction to phonic skills needed for identifying the vocabulary of the selections
2. Introduction to thinking abilities required for the satisfactory comprehension of the selections

Purposes

These activities serve two purposes:

1. *New skills.* For teaching new skills when they are needed
2. *Self help.* As a source of self help for the pupil

The sequence for teaching new skills and reviewing them is detailed in *The ABC Teacher's Guide: Third Reader (3-2).* In addition, specific suggestions for teaching new skills are given in both the teacher's guide and the teacher's edition of this storybook, providing the busy teacher with practical help at the right time.

Use

Activities in this section of the book are used after the first (silent) reading of a selection. About three to five minutes are required for each one.

The phonics-thinking pages at the end of each unit of this book are used to:

1. Teach new phonic-thinking skills
2. Review learnings
3. Help the pupil to apply skills to selected words from the next unit

For pupils who need additional help, these phonics-thinking pages may be used with one or more of the following:

Betts-Welch ABC Phonic Charts

Betts-Welch Study Book for *The ABC Along Friendly Roads*

Pathways to Phonic Skills (recordings)

PHONIC SKILLS: AUTOMATIC USE

Children can be taught to use phonic skills and other word-learning skills automatically. When the use of these skills is automatic, pupils can then give their attention to the real purpose of reading: getting the thought.

Teaching New Skills

Teaching new phonic skills is done by having the pupils follow four easy steps:

1. Listen to the sound of the letter or syllable phonogram in the spoken word; e.g., the sound of *ou*\ aü\ in *thousand,* of *dg*\ j\ in *judging, ly* \ -lē\ of *lovely*
2. Say the vowel sound of the syllable
3. Identify the letters of the phonogram representing the sound or syllable
4. Check the use, or meaning, of the word in its sentence setting

Application of Skills

Teaching the *application* of phonic skills during silent reading-study activities is done by having the pupils:

1. Identify the unknown phonogram in the printed word
2. Recall the sound (s) represented by the phonogram
3. Identify the meaning of the word in its sentence

Specific suggestions for teaching the pupil to use his phonic skills automatically are given in the Teachers Edition: Annotated and Keyed.

THINKING

In this storybook, the thinking and phonic activities are carefully interwoven. For example, the study of last syllables *ar* and *or* and compound words contributes to the pupil's (1) correct usage of words and (2) phonic skills.

Introducing New Learnings

This development of new learnings is done by having the pupil follow two steps:

1. Relate the purpose of the activity to the selection in this storybook
2. Complete the activity and identify—when practical—similar situations in the selection

Application of Learnings

New learnings are applied by the pupil during his silent reading and in activities following the silent and/or rereading. Silent and oral rereading afford many opportunities to interpret punctuation, discuss shifts of meanings of words, and make other applications.

CHILD LEARNINGS

This basic reading-study program helps the pupil (1) to mature in his *interests,* (2) to make automatic use of *phonic* skills and (3) to develop *concepts* and *thinking* abilities which insure comprehension. Detailed suggestions for achieving these goals are given in *The ABC Teacher's Guide: Third Reader (3-2).*

All previously taught skills are maintained in this book. (See Teacher's Edition: Annotated and Keyed.) New skills follow:

Phonics (letters and syllables)

1. Consonant sounds and their phonograms; e.g.,\ sh\ sound of *sh* in *shape, s* in *sugar,* and *c* of *special;*\ch\ sound *ch* in *such, tch* in *watch,* and *t* in *adventure;*\f\sound of *f* in *fog, ph* in *telegraph,* and *gh* in *enough*

2. Consonant phonograms and their sounds; e.g., *ng*\ng\of *hang* and *nk*\ngk\ of *think*
3. Stressed first syllables in most two-syllable words
4. Unstressed last syllables: e.g., *age*\ -ij\of *village;* unstressed first syllables: e.g., *de*\dē\of *decide, ex*\iks\ of *exclaim, in* \ in\ of *insist, re*\ rē\of *receive*

Thinking

1. Sentence analysis: subordinate clauses
2. Suffix *less,* as in *hairless*
3. Prefix *un,* as in *unbroken* and *unloaded*
4. Shifts in the meanings and uses of words; e.g., *run, land*
5. Idiomatic expressions; e.g., *keep his word*

Here are three vowel rules you have learned.

1. In words like **dig** and **ten,** the short sound of the one vowel is heard.

2. In words like **face** and **ice,** the long sound of the first vowel is heard. The last letter **e** is silent.

3. In words like **cream** and **wait,** the long sound of the first vowel is heard. The second vowel is silent.

Use the above rules to study the following words. First, look at the vowel letters and decide which rule can help you. Then say the word and use it in a sentence.

Pages 6–12

Jim	state	cross
end	sea	wait

Pages 14–19

ship	chain	sand
lock	hide	chest

Pages 20–25

sang	leap	straight
kept	fox	swam

Pages 26–32

queen	drop	free
bee	lip	hope

Which words are pictured?

Root Word	Changed Word	Kind of Change
drop	dropping	**+ p + ing**
hide	hiding	take away **e; + ing**
thought	thoughtful	**+ ful**
safe	safer	**+ r**
love	lovely	**+ ly**
teach	teacher	**+ er**

Study the root words, the changed words, and the kinds of changes above.

Now say each root word that follows. Find the word at the right that was made from the root word. How are both words used?

Pages 33–39

row*e r* The rower grew tired as he neared the tower on the bridge.

color*ful* Jane was wearing a colorful jacket and a new leather cap.

Pages 40–45

quiet *ly* Grandfather went quietly into the room and put another blanket on Tom.

map *ping* The men were carefully mapping the country around the camp.

Pages 46–52

ripe *er* Gus said the peach in his hand was riper than the one on the tree.

skate *ing* The boys were skating yesterday.

331

Vowel letters are **a, e, i, o, u,** and sometimes **w** and **y.** The other letters are consonants.

Look at the word **paw.** The first letter is the consonant **p.** The rest of the word is **aw.** Look at the word **teach.** The first consonant is **t.** The rest of the word is **each.**

Now put the **p** of **paw** with the **each** of **teach** to make another word. Find the word you made.

The fruit that Jenny likes best

is the peach.

Make some words from two others you know. Use only the first consonants of the first words. Use the last parts of the second words to make the words at the right.

Pages 54–60

| chain | deer | cheer |
| shook | feet | sheet |

Pages 61–67

start	cream	steam
ripe	face	race
slept	row	slow

Pages 68–73

full	red	fed
life	cap	lap
spoke	still	spill

Which words are pictured?

332

Root Word	Changed Word	Kind of Change
lap	lapped	**+ p + ed**
skate	skater	**+ r**
puppy	puppies	**y** to **i; + es**
cry	cried	**y** to **i; + ed**
big	biggest	**+ g + est**

Study the root words, the changed words, and the kinds of changes above.

Now say each root word that follows. Find the word at the right that was made from the root word. How are both words used?

Pages 74–80

settle — Every settler in the fort was ready to fight the Indians.

Pages 81, 82–88

fiddle — Jack and the fiddler were wearing ties that looked alike.

try — The peddler tried to tie the ribbon around Nancy's head.

Pages 89–92

sad — Daniel told the saddest tale that Jack had ever heard.

pony — The ponies had escaped from the barn and were out of sight.

skin — Dusty skinned the bear and hurried home with the meat.

Say each word at the right **in**
and listen to the number of **invent**
vowel sounds in each one. **invented**

In has one vowel sound and only one syllable.
Invent has two vowel sounds and two syllables.
Invented has three vowel sounds and three syllables.

Here are some words you know. Say each word and decide how many syllables it has.

pass	insisted	duck	turkey
passenger	lifted	motor	Kentucky
danger	in	conductor	hen

Here are pairs of words for you to say. You know the first word, and it will help you say the new word.

Pages 93–99

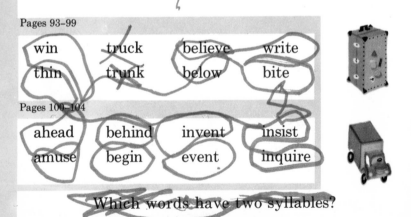

win truck believe write
thin trunk below bite

Pages 100–104

ahead behind invent insist
amuse begin event inquire

Which words have two syllables?
Which words are pictured?

334

Use a helping word to say a new word. The helping word has the same vowel sound as the first syllable of the new word.

Helping word: **got**

New word: **cotton**

Cotton _____ .

grows   bites

Helping word: **pick**

New word: **nickel**

A nickel is _____ .

ribbon   money

Helping word: **mouth**

New word: **thousand**

Thousand is a _____ .

number   state

Helping word: **trick**

New word: **cricket**

A cricket is an _____ .

insect   island

Helping word: **bread**

New word: **breakfast**

You _____ breakfast.

hum   eat

Helping word: **say**

New word: **famous**

A _____ may be famous.

man   poke

Helping word: **low**

New word: **cozy**

Cozy means _____ .

warm   greedy

Helping word: **bat**

New word: **attic**

An attic is in a _____ .

hive   house

Each word at the left below has two syllables.
Look at the first vowel letter and decide if its
sound is likely to be long or short. Then say the
word and find another word at the right with
the same vowel sound.

princess	plan	thin	hum	vine
fifteen	drift	net	fact	trail
spinning	frog	life	gull	spill
disturb	spoke	hive	slip	sell

Pages 146–152

| baggage | plain | add | swish | knock |
| silly | wide | wreck | will | stone |

Pages 153–160

| season | press | flame | flood | stream |
| rustle | drip | Gus | job | boot |

Which words are pictured below?

Use a helping word to say a longer word. The
helping word has the same vowel sound as the
second syllable of the longer word.

Helping word: **plain**

explain

Explain means to _____ clearly.

tell shoot

Helping word: **spend**

depend

To depend on
someone means
to _____ on him.

pound count

Helping word: **tribe**

describe

To describe
something means
to _____ about it.

inquire tell

Helping word: **lap**

perhaps

Perhaps means _____.

maybe proved

Helping word: **wide**

beside

Beside means _____.

near far

Helping word: **deck**

forget

If you forget, you do not _____.

depend remember

337

When you hear the word **pencil,** one syllable sounds stronger than the other. Say **pencil,** and listen for that syllable.

The first syllable of **pencil** sounds stronger. That syllable is called the accented one. Say the words below and listen for the accented syllable of each one.

silver   person   autumn   butter

The first syllable of each word is accented. This is true of most words with two syllables.

Now say the words below. Find the one word in each row that does not have the first syllable accented.

special   approach   middle   Friday
prairie   sugar   season   become

Here are some pairs of words for you to say. You know the first word. It will help you say the accented syllable of the second word.

list   tea   most   fine
blizzard   tepee   moment   final

Which word is pictured?

The following facts may help you say the first syllables of new words.

1. The first syllable may sound just like a one-syllable word you know, as **but** in **butter**.
2. The first syllable may have the same vowel sound as a one-syllable word you know, as **ten** and **pencil**.

Study the pairs of words below. Use one of the facts you have studied to help you say the new words.

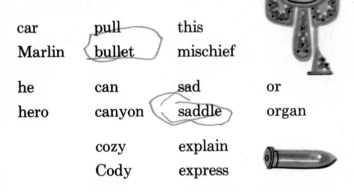

car	pull	this
Marlin	bullet	mischief
he	can	sad	or
hero	canyon	saddle	organ
	cozy	explain
	Cody	express

Which new words are pictured?

Syllables that are not accented are called unaccented. Here are three different kinds.

Pages 214–220

With l

Words you know: **circle, cattle, uncle**
New word: **chuckle**
A chuckle is a laughing sound.

Pages 221–227

With y

Words you know: **lady, lucky, merry**
New word: **berry**
A berry is a kind of fruit.

Pages 228–235

With r

Words you know: **color, supper, quarter**
New word: **eager**
To be eager means to want very much to do something.

Here are some words you know. Say each word and decide how many syllables it has.

twenty	go	fish	holiday
ten	amigo	disappear	hollow
adventure	hero	Spanish	hop

Here are pairs of words with the same number of syllables. You know the first word, and it will help you say the new word.

change	wonder	whistle	dance
range	thunder	whisper	chance

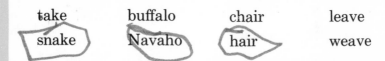

Pages 244–250

take	buffalo	chair	leave
snake	Navaho	hair	weave

Pages 251–257

describe	cap	wheat	sniff
descend	trap	heat	cliff

Which words have three syllables?
Which new words are pictured?

341

Read the following sentences and notice how the syllable **un** changes each word at the left.

happy

Rita became unhappy when she lost her pretty silk handkerchief.

easy

The cowboy felt uneasy when he looked down and saw a snake in his boot.

discovered

For almost a week the robber remained undiscovered in Hawk Hollow.

kind

The fellow boasted that he had never been unkind to any animal —wild or tame.

Read the following sentences and notice how the syllable **re** changes each word at the left.

filled

The glass was soon empty and Nancy asked to have it refilled with milk.

visit

The handsome gentleman said, "I have come to revisit the place where I was born."

paint

Jack said, "Let's either repaint this chair or throw it away."

join

Bill said to the trapped creature, "I intend to free you and let you rejoin your family in the woods."

Tell why each word below has only one vowel sound. If you don't remember, use the help given after each word.

1. blast (One vowel letter—one sound)
2. dream (Two vowels side by side—one sound)
3. sharp (Vowels followed by **r**—one sound)
4. spike (Silent final **e**—one sound of first vowel)
5. tool (Two vowels, usual sound—one sound)

Now use what you know to decide how many syllables a word has. Count the number of places where one vowel sound is likely to be heard, and you know the number of syllables.

Do that with each word below. The first one is done for you.

Ricardo 3	gravel	beyond
engineer	boulder	locomotive
handsome	either	boast

Which words are pictured?

course 1	post	excuse
enjoy	rather	gay
elephant	polite	folks

Which word means a kind of animal?

Which word means "to have a good time"?

Which word means the same as **merry**?

Here are three words you know. Say each one and listen for the syllable that is the same in each one.

depend   descend   describe

Which syllable is the same in each word?

Study the following rows of words in the same way. Say the words across each row. Decide which syllable is the same.

alarm	amuse	against
beside	between	believe
insist	instead	invent
excuse	exclaim	express

In each sentence below find a word that begins with the syllable **a, be, de, ex,** or **in.**

Jack would not agree with Tony that the goat was strong enough to pull the cart.

Miss Shore started to explain that grease is often used to make soap.

Jane cried, "If I see one flash of lightning, I intend to run for the house."

Don was angry at his pet because the little burro would not move an inch.

Mr. Ricardo greeted Pedro with delight at the garden gate.

Are you ready for the next book?

1. Say each word across the first row. Then find its root word in the second row.

| politely | trading | ladies | trapped |
| trap | lady | polite | trade |

2. How many syllables does each word have?

| knight | parachute | tinder | editor |

3. Say each word across the first row and listen to the vowel sound in the first syllable. Then find a word in the second row with the same vowel sound.

| written | creature | handsome | hogan |
| coast | grand | steel | whip |

4. Say each word across the first row and listen to the vowel sound in the second syllable. Then find a word in the second row with the same vowel sound.

| suppose | polite | invent | alarm |
| pipe | spark | post | spend |

5. Which syllable is accented in these words?

| lightning | burro | boulder | polite |
| needle | excuse | habit | thunder |

6. What new word is made from the first syllable of **captain** and the second syllable of **picture?**

comfort   cocker   capture

345

Jane and Pat Warner lived near the place where the river ran into a big lake.
Jane and Pat lived near what place?

The children thought the bridge was the most beautiful one in the world.
What did the children think?

As soon as their mother went to the store, the children looked in the big order book.
When did the children look in the big book?

Captain Peters was master of the large bridge which stood where the lake and the river met.
Where was the bridge?

The children did not tell the captain they needed to earn money to buy a jacket for their mother.
What did the children keep secret?
Why did they need to earn money?

Because the children looked so sad, Captain Peters went on to say, "I'll tell you how it is."
Why did Captain Peters go on to say something?
What did he say?

The Interesting Opossum

What does an opossum like to eat?

How many baby opossums may a mother have at one time?

Why do opossums hunt at night?

What does "playing 'possum" mean?

In what way is an opossum's tail useful?

Which questions are answered below? Where?

An opossum is different in some ways from all other animals in this country. As many as ten babies ride around on the mother's back until they are able to go out on their own.

A mother opossum is about as large as a cat. Her head is small. Her tail is long, like a rat's tail, and very helpful in climbing. She has two coats of fur: one is soft and short, close to her skin; the other is long and gray.

During the day every opossum is a sleepyhead. At night, however, it hunts for birds, frogs, fish, eggs, insects, and fruit. If it is not careful, the slow opossum may be the supper of another animal—wolf, wildcat, fox, or bear.

When surprised by a hunter, the opossum often stays very still for a long time. This trick of showing no life is called "playing 'possum."

Facts or Feelings

Pokey thought that the Mississippi River was the greatest in the world.

The above sentence tells you of Pokey's **feelings** about the Mississippi River. It states one boy's **feeling**, not a **fact**.

The Mississippi River is the second largest in the world.

A book of **facts** tells you that the Mississippi River is the largest one in the United States. Moreover, it tells you it is one of the longest in the world—only one other being longer.

The Cotton Picking Contest was the most exciting event of the year.

The town of Greenbanks was thirty miles from the farm.

Pokey thought the top pocket of his overalls would be a safe place for his money.

The number of leaves in the cotton pickings was used by the judges for deciding how clean they were.

To Pokey, it seemed hours before the judges decided on the winners.

Which Meaning?

Page 146	**telegraph**	**1** A way of sending news over electric wires. **2** To send by telegraph.
Page 147	**cross**	**1** Any drawing made by the crossing of two straight lines. **2** To move across; as, to *cross* the river. **3** Mean; almost angry.
Page 148	**baggage**	**1** Trunks, boxes, and the like that one takes on a trip. **2** Explaining a kind of car or room in which trunks are stored.
Page 149	**press**	**1** To bear down upon. **2** Any machine by which something is pressed; as, a printing *press*.
Page 150	**copy**	**1** One of a great number made at the same printing. **2** To make a copy.
Page 151	**spread**	**1** To flow out or over. **2** A cover for a table or bed.
Page 152	**rest**	**1** Sleep. **2** The part that is left over. **3** The other, those not named.

Using Facts for Thinking

Big John liked life on the river. He stood at a big wheel all day long. His job was to keep the boat going in the right direction. Then, too, he had to keep the boat from hitting rocks and running into a mud bank.

What was Big John called?

In most parts of our country there comes a time of the year when the trees lose their leaves. Farmers gather their corn, apples, pumpkins, and other crops. Children amuse themselves by cutting out faces on pumpkins and lighting them with candles for Halloween. Birds fly south to warmer weather.

Which season of the year is described?

Often the sun shines. At other times there is fog, rain, or snow. When big black clouds roll in, they tell of a coming storm. Sometimes, too, strong winds rush across land and sea.

What are all of these changes called?

Below is a listing of ideas from the story "The Mule-eared Squirrel," pages 206-212. Notice the heading and the fact that each part of the listing belongs under that heading. Moreover, each part is listed in the order in which it is told in the story.

People in the Camp

Joe Hall, the cook

Polaski, the leader

Other workmen

The stranger with the money

Two robbers

Now study the three different lists of ideas below. In each list decide which idea is the chief one and make it the heading. Then put the other ideas under it in the order they are told in the story.

Bobcats, Rabbits, Animals, Squirrel

Cans of food, Things the Robbers Tried to Take, Paper money

Tin plates, Mouth organ, Bullets, Things Jack Liked to Hide, Knives

In the first sentence of each pair below, the answer is given in heavy, dark print along with underlined parts that help you know the answer. Find an answer for the second sentence that goes with its underlined part in the same way.

Proud Pirate was as **swift** as if he had winged hoofs.

Like a red-brown ____ the stallion would rush up to a herd of tame horses.

    toss   flash   shade

"Sh-h-h-h! It's Proud Pirate and his herd of horses," Tom said in a **whisper**.

Tom had heard about Proud Pirate, the fearless ____ of Wild River Canyon.

    stallion   donkey   language

The cowboys were going out on the **range** the next day to search for wild horses.

Wild horses made fine ranch horses once they were caught and ____ .

    tasted   searched   tamed

One of the ranchers, **Mr. Hall**, had offered two steers to anyone who could rope Pirate.

A sound like ____ came across the range.

    breath   twenty   thunder

When Mr. Jones and B Good reached town, they noticed many trees had been blown down.

In the above sentence **many** does not tell the number of trees. However, you may guess the number. Two, fifty, or a thousand?

Since a thousand would be more trees than you'd be likely to find in a small town, you wouldn't guess that number. Two trees would not be **many.** A better guess would be about fifty.

Mr. Jones gave B Good a quarter to buy a new handle for the saw.

You know how much money B Good had because a quarter is twenty-five cents.

Which ideas below tell you how much or how many? Which ideas suggest that you guess?

Mr. Jones told Mr. Silverwand that his saw handle was broken and he needed a new one.

After the magic saw went to work, all the trees on Weaver Street were cut up.

Ricardo thought it would take several men to lift the great boulder.

Ricardo's father said, "That boulder has been there for years."

One locomotive pulled in front and two more locomotives pushed from behind.

THE ABC Along Friendly Roads

NEW WORDS: 338   CUMULATIVE VOCABULARY: 1359

TOTAL VOCABULARY FOR *The ABC Beyond Treasure Valley*
AND *The ABC Along Friendly Roads:* 640

The ABC Along Friendly Roads follows *The ABC On Our Way, The ABC Time to Play, The ABC All in a Day, The ABC Up the Street and Down, The ABC Around Green Hills, The ABC Down Singing River, The ABC Over a City Bridge,* and *The ABC Beyond Treasure Valley.*

The ABC Along Friendly Roads and the accompanying study book introduce and develop the 640 words listed below.

A unique program for developing and extending phonic and thinking skills is given on pages 330-353 of the book. In addition, the ABC Phonic Charts and Pathways to Phonic Skills (recordings) may be used for both individualized and group activities.

Specific suggestions for using this book and the accompanying study book are given in the Teacher's Guide.

The vocabulary chart below indicates the page on which each of the 338 new words is introduced in *The ABC Along Friendly Roads.* Each of the 302 words used in *The ABC Beyond Treasure Valley* is indicated by an asterisk (*). These words are introduced and maintained as "new" words in this book.

All variants of a word are counted as new words, with the following exceptions: singular and plural possessives; words ending in *s, d, ed, es, ing, er* (comparison), *est,* and *r* (comparison); those in which the final consonant is doubled, the final *e* is dropped, the final *le* is dropped, the final *y* is changed to *i,* or the final *f* is changed to *v.* Compounds of two known words and contractions from which one letter is omitted are not counted as new words. In addition, exceptions are made for words ending in the suffixes *y, er* (agent), *ly, r* (agent), *ful, en, n,* and *less,* and for those beginning with the prefixes *un* and *re.*

UNIT I	14. treasure*	21. leaped	28. laws
6. Jim*	pirates	straight*	against
state*	ship*	22. often*	29. became
crossed*	sand*	mouth*	free*
7. world	15. captain*	warned	angry*
most*	Tom*	23. squirrel*	30. lip
interesting	Maine	fear	Jenny*
8. cameras*	16. buried	24. fox*	bees
end*	shovel*	swam	31. mind*
9. great*	hide	25. body*	32. repeat
united*	17. chest*	promise	33. Jane*
beautiful*	jewels	kept*	lake*
10.	18. chain*	26. queen*	jacket
11.	lock	Alice	34. gifts
12. studying*	glittering*	prince*	cents*
ocean*	19. bundles	insisted	banks*
sea*	20. sang	27. drop*	earn
13.	deer*	castle*	

354

35. row*
    towers
36. dust*
    ten*
    offer*
37. lifted*
    motor
38. repair
    quick*
39. . . . .
40. turkeys
    market*
    flock
    map
41. switch
    blankets*
    insects
42. camp
    slept
    village*
43. sight*
    full
    dry
44. quiet*
    feels*
    means*
45. . . . .
46. Gus
    islands*
    peach
47. life*
    bad*
    thumb
48. ripe*
    spoil
    invented
49. shook*
50. tomorrow*
    matter
    skates*
    ticket
51. crop*
52. yesterday

UNIT II

53. . . . .
54. ghost
    grandmother*
    visit*

55. spoke*
    conductor
    passengers
56. during*
    dining
    different*
57. . . . .
58. hollowed
    gathered*
    favors
59. candle
60. cheers*
    moaning
    sheet
61. engine*
    steam*
    steep*
62. Cooper
    worth*
63. women
    thirty*
    history
64. robber*
    puffing*
    excited*
65. coals
    waved*
    raced*
66. coach*
    slow*
67. . . . .
68. sigh*
    orange*
    between*
69. fed
    pillow
    lap
70. scratching
    ears*
    cry*
71. spilled
    knocked*
    porches*
    chewed
72. taught
    disappeared*
73. we'll
74. Kentucky
    Boone
    valley*
    Daniel

75. settle*
    walls*
    fort
    Indians*
76. guns*
    fight
77. lead*
    tunnel
78. burning*
    arrows*
    danger*
    saved*
79. . . . .
80. . . . .
81. alike
    wing*
82. Nancy*
    tea
    even*
    sick
83. trail*
    chicken
    roast*
    company*
84. cabin*
    peddler's
    ribbons
85. sneeze*
    kettle*
    hook
86. knife
87. fiddle
88. . . . .
89. tale
    word*
    trouble*
    pony*
90. load
    meat
    pound
    wild*
91. bushes
    claws
    acts
    roar*
92. escape
    hundred*
    fur*
    skin*

93. raccoon*
    neck*
    teeth*
    trunk
94. opossums
    thin
    below
95. crawled*
    turtle*
    swamp
    frightened*
96. mud*
    frog*
    trembled
97. shone
    bite
98. . . . .
99. . . . .
100. forest*
     break
     amused
101. such*
     harm
     arrive
     begin
102. explain*
     event
     fact*
103. net
     adding*
104. inquired
     replied*

UNIT III

105. . . . .
106. poke
     cotton
     Mississippi
107. lose*
     spend*
     gulls*
108. contest*
     nickel
     pocket*
109. judges*
     thousand
     receive*
110. pop
     speeding
111. . . . .

355

112. shoulder
clean*
113. . . . .
114. bought*
honey*
hives
115. themselves
sting
116. tunes
hum
117. imitate
crickets
low*
118. television*
meet*
119. delighted
plans*
stage*
120. sell*
121. Pepperminta
belonged
122. Bob*
wrecked
noticed*
123. breakfast
star*
sweet*
124. zoo*
125. famous
vines*
done*
126. drove
forgot*
thick*
127. greedy
128. . . . .
129. Susan*
130. floods
boots
slip*
131. stove*
cozy
worst
worry*
132. flowing*
attic
straw*
133. drifting*
134. inches
splashed*
signal*

135. pilot*
136. beauty
137. twelve
princess*
rose*
wand
138. feast
touches*
fifteen*
spinning
139. dead
awake
140. lazy*
141. lies
142. disturb
stone*
tear
143. . . . .
144. drip
stream
145. plain*
wide*
swish*
146. Edison
telegraph
147. experiments
wire
job*
148. baggage
these*
vegetables*
149. chemicals
press
150. threw
silly*
copy
151. spread
flames
152. electric*
153. Winnebago
tribe*
cranberry
154. fawn
shy
sticks*
155. roots*
156. weather*
packed
built*
157. season
songs

158. shoot*
rustle
159. mine*
prove
160. . . . .

UNIT IV
161. . . . .
162. prairie*
guided
deck*
163. steering
described*
Friday*
fog*
164. depends
clouds*
165. . . . .
166. held*
sniffed*
mixing
167. else
sugar
butter*
wharf*
168. . . . .
169. middle*
hired
earth
170. perhaps*
jeans
mailing*
besides*
171. bowl*
list*
pencil
172. mules
173. won't
174. . . . .
175. . . . .
176. person
lend
jelly*
177. shelf
case
forget
178. sold
wool*
Jones*
179. special*

180. jar*
stripes
silver*
beads
181. bow*
182. . . . .
183. . . . .
184. wheat*
185. autumn
approaching
cool
186. freeze
months*
sets*
187. becomes
born
188. holidays
189. Paul
blizzard
190. beat
scared*
moment*
191. finally*
remaining
192. agreed*
decorations
hanging
193. . . . .
194. draw*
tepee
195. shape*
understand*
196. . . . .
197. halls
198. Cody
buffaloes
express
199. canyons
hid*
saddle
200. hoofs
galloped*
Marlin
201. bending
202. distance*
narrow
throw*
203. . . . .
204. bullet
adventure*
hero

356

205. . . . .
206. favorite
log*
joy
shine*
207. music
organ
208. lying*
tin*
branch
pile*
209. . . . .
210. creep*
heart
211. rope*
searched
bang*
212. mischief

UNIT V

213. . . . .
214. ranch*
Texas
circle*
cattle*
215. wake
chuckled
you'll
216. silence
since*
217. speak
herd
begged
218. shut
gumdrops
219. leaned
tasted
220. . . . .
221. carol
luck*
222. cousins
merry*
join
223. instead*
stocking
224. berry
shades
225. ages
226. discovered*
stared
lady*

227. entered
228. Mexico
although*
quarter*
souvenir
229. *amiga*
price*
Spanish
language*
230. choose
perfect*
231. clay
232. twenty
donkey*
233. Rita
eager
234. . . . .
235. *amigo*
236. range
tamed
237. thunder
stallion
kicking
238. smart
swift*
239. neigh
whispered
240. ledge
smooth
stretched*
241. chance
242. breath*
wise*
toss*
243. . . . .
244. Navaho
snakes
desert*
sheep*
245. juniper
handkerchief
lambs
246. hair
smoke*
hogans
247. rattles*
dawn*
248. folded
249. I'd
chief*
250. weave

251. cliffs
descended
252. gentle*
mole*
253. path
trap
254. several
continued*
nests
255. heat
hawk*
coyote*
256. crept
growl
257. blind*
rays*
258. fancy
silk*
whip
handle*
259. boast
260. fellows*
bunks
interrupted
261. howled*
skunk
suggest
262. desperate
263. intend
easy
terrible*
264. . . . .
265. trade*
habit
sharp*
266. cactus*
collection
handsome
267. creatures
alarm
268. bold*
269. . . . .
270. needles*
271. line*
tool*
272. either

UNIT VI

273. . . . .
274. Ricardo
lonely*
locomotive

275. geography
dreamed*
engineer
276. spikes*
loose
gravel
277. boulder
California
278. shrieked
blasts
279. fierce*
280. flare
281. beyond*
282. post*
Jingle's
enjoy*
283. elephants*
course*
gay
284. rather
mad*
polite
nod*
285. grunted*
forth*
folks
286. excuses
snap*
287. . . . .
288. . . . .
289. grand
290. . . . .
291. shore*
Tony*
cart
292. we'd
soap
293. supposed*
pipe*
grease*
294. foam
295. . . . .
296. . . . .
297. already
298. . . . .
299. Pedro
Don*
gate*
300. burro
301. brayed

357

302. . . . .

303. . . . .

304. crash
   lightning
   greet*

305. . . . .

306. . . . .

307. . . . .

308. . . . .

309. brass
   knight

310. steel
   tinder

311. written

312. . . . .

313. . . . .

314. . . . .

315. Oregon
   mirror

316. parachute

317. you've

318. spark*

319. . . . .

320. . . . .

321. . . . .

322. . . . .

323. coast*
   editor

324. type

325. pages*

326. teletype

327. . . . .

328. . . . .

329. . . . .

PHONICS: pages 330–345

Thinking Activities: pages 346–353

358

ACKNOWLEDGMENTS

Grateful acknowledgment is made for permission to adapt and use the following copyrighted material:

"A Letter from Grandfather" from "Circle of the Seasons" by Glenn O. Blough, in *Jack and Jill*, October, 1941; used by permission of the author.

"A Carol for the Mayor" from "A Carol for the Governor" by Rebecca Caudill, in *Trails for Juniors*, published by The Methodist Publishing House; used by permission of the author.

"Bright-Eyes, the Little Raccoon" from "The Adventures of Lotor" by Allen Chaffee, in *Children's Activities*, September, 1941; used by permission of the author.

"A Tall Tale from the High Hills" by Ellis Credle, in *Story Parade*, August, 1946; used by permission of the author.

"The Mule-eared Squirrel" by George Cory Franklin, in *Child Life;* used by permission of the author.

"The Wonderful Saw," adapted from "Grandpa Toggle's Wonderful Saw" by Robert L. Grimes, from *Grandpa Toggle's Wonderful Book*, published by The Caxton Printers, Ltd., Caldwell, Idaho; used by permission of the copyright owners.

"Step-Along" from *Susie* by May Justus, published by Albert Whitman & Company; used by permission of the author.

"The Long Road to Rivertown" by Elizabeth Coatsworth; used by permission of Alfred A. Knopf, Inc.

"The Treasure Hunt" by Berta and Elmer Hader; used by permission of The Macmillan Company.

"Sandy Does the Wash" by Neil Anderson; reprinted by permission of Julian Messner, Inc., from *Meet Sandy Smith* by Neil Anderson; copyright date May 6, 1954, by Jerrold Beim.

"A Day in Mexico" from "Mexican Souvenir" by Belle Coates; reprinted from December, 1946 issue of *Jr. Language and Arts*, by permission of Progressive Educators, Inc.

"The Moving House" by Dorothy Aldis; used by permission of G. P. Putnam's Sons.

"Holding Hands" by Lenore M. Link, in *St. Nicholas*, June, 1936; used by permission of Mrs. J. David Stern.

"The King of Smithland" from "The King of Smithia" by Walter R. Brooks; "King of the Range" by Margaret Jamison, copyright, 1947, by Story Parade, Inc.; "How the Bridge Helped" by Mildred Lawrence; "Far-off Places" by Earl M. Rush, copyright, 1946, by Story Parade, Inc.; and "Three Cheers! It's Spring!" from "Presto! It's Spring" by Earl Marvin Rush, copyright, 1947, by Story Parade, Inc.; adapted by permission of Story Parade, Inc.

"Bill Cody, Winner of the West" from *Buffalo Bill* by Frank L. Beals, and "New Homes in Kentucky" from *Daniel Boone* by Edna McGuire, in the "American Adventure Series;" used by permission of the Wheeler Publishing Company.